Life & Love

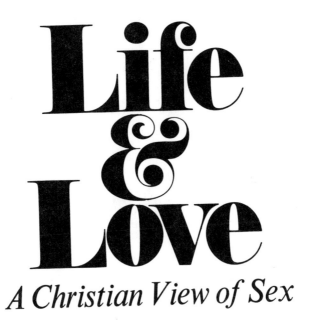

Life & Love

A Christian View of Sex

Clyde M. Narramore

ZONDERVAN PUBLISHING HOUSE

GRAND RAPIDS   MICHIGAN

LIFE AND LOVE
Copyright 1956 by
Clyde M. Narramore

First printing............July, 1956
Second printing......December, 1956
Third printing......September, 1957
Fourth printing........October, 1958
Fifth printing............May, 1959
Sixth printing............May, 1959
Seventh printing.....September, 1960
Eighth printing........August, 1961
Ninth printing.................1963
Tenth printing.................1964
Eleventh printing........May, 1965
Twelfth printing......October, 1965
Thirteenth printing...December, 1965
Fourteenth printing ....January, 1967
Fifteenth printing.....February, 1968
Sixteenth printing......October, 1968
Seventeenth printing.......June, 1969
Eighteenth printing.....January, 1970
Nineteenth printing........May, 1970
Twentieth printing .....October, 1970
More than 200,000 copies in print

Printed in the United States of America

ACKNOWLEDGMENTS

The preparation of this book has been a cooperative effort. Many people have made valuable contributions to its development. Educators, Christian journalists, homemakers, marriage counselors, medical doctors and ministers have been of special assistance.

Appreciation is expressed here to many young people throughout America with whom the author has carried on research studies. These findings have been valuable as a foundation for the book.

Special appreciation and gratitude is expressed here to the following who have made this publication possible: Jonathan E. Braun, Dr. Walter C. Engel, Dr. Leland Glover, Dr. E. J. Halley, Dorothy C. Haskin, Rev. Ray Heimbeck, Dr. John L. Jackson, Ruth E. Narramore, W. Roberts Pedrick, Evelyn W. Rutherford, Bruce Shelley, Dr. Robert T. Sutherland, Georgiana Walker, and Dr. Charles J. Woodbridge.

Grateful appreciation is expressed to Dr. Lester F. Beck, for permission to base the schematic drawings in this book on the illustrations in his book, *Human Growth.*

TABLE OF CONTENTS

LIST OF ILLUSTRATIONS

1

Youth Talk it Over

"Courtship and Marriage" was the title of a series of meetings for young people, sponsored by the Wilton Avenue Church. The discussion leader found that this, his third meeting, was being enjoyed by all the group which was composed mostly of Christians.

The leader realized that these young people were at an important age. They were making decisions which would mold their lives. The leader was helping them gain insights into the causes of their behavior.

His purpose in presenting the next portion of the program was to help them identify their own problems and motives, in order that they might better understand themselves and in turn, make wiser decisions.

"Now," he said, "I'd like to tell you some reaction stories — some short but important statements about young people. As soon as I finish each one," he added, "I would like you to tell why the fellows and girls in the story acted as they did. Ready?"

☆　*Shirley is a good-looking girl who makes top grades but doesn't have many close friends.*

QUESTION: WHY DOESN'T SHIRLEY HAVE MANY CLOSE FRIENDS?

RONNIE: It's my guess that she's so wrapped up in her studies that she can't think of anything else. That would set her off from the group. She probably spends too much time studying and not enough "socializing."

SANDRA: She may have an inferiority complex, and yet if she's both smart and pretty I don't see how she could — unless, well, unless maybe she has an older sister or someone who makes fun of her. That could be.

CHUCK: She probably has a *superiority* complex toward the others who aren't so smart.

KARIN: I don't think being smart should hinder her. You can be real smart and still have lots of friends. I doubt if she's learned how to get along with people.

DAVE: I've been wondering about something else. We don't know whether she's a Christian or not. But if she were, it should really help her to be more friendly. If she *is* a Christian, I'd say she hasn't given the Lord a chance to change her.

JOE: That might be, but maybe all through school she's made the other kids jealous, and now that she is growing up she realizes it. So now she's touchy about being "a brain" and just clams up when she's around other kids.

LEO: Brains and looks don't always make a girl popular. She could have both and still be a flat tire if she's not the kind of person who's fun to be with.

Bruce: I think the guys are envious of her good grades.

Jacque: Do you mean to say there are some boys who haven't found out that girls are smarter than boys?

☆ *Bill and Carolyn had dated quite a long time when Carolyn said, "Maybe I shouldn't say this Bill, but since I don't go out with anyone else I don't think it's fair for you to either."*

Question: Why didn't Carolyn want Bill to date anyone else?

Pat: I'll bet she's the possessive type — a few dates and she thinks she owns him.

Ronnie: She probably didn't have as many opportunities for dates as he did.

Jacque: It looks to me like she was afraid of losing him. She wasn't sure of herself.

Joe: I know girls that test a guy just by using that method. They want to know if he's worth getting serious over.

Pat: It looks to me as if she were already pretty serious. Maybe she suspects he isn't so serious, and she just wants to settle it, that's all. No one likes a one-sided affair.

Chuck: She probably really wanted this guy to like her. All that mattered was that she hooked him. But take it from me, she needs a few lessons on how to do it!

Bruce: I don't imagine she got much affection when she was growing up. When she finally found this fellow who responded by giving her affection she didn't want to share him with anyone.

HAL: I think that Ronnie was partly right about her not having as many opportunities for dates as he did. She just didn't want him to be getting away with anything that she wasn't.

BETTY: But girls are at a disadvantage. They have to wait to be asked out, and sometimes they aren't. You fellows have more freedom in dating. It's not fair.

DAVE: This whole question about Bill and Carolyn is simple! Anyone can see that it's just her sly way of asking him to go "steady." I'd never be taken in by that one.

☆ *Helen has dated Lee several times. They have decided to go steady but Helen's parents don't want her to.*

QUESTION: WHY DON'T HELEN'S PARENTS WANT HER TO GO STEADY?

SANDRA: They probably feel she is too young to know what's best for her. They want her to be free to know more boys before she gets too serious over one.

STEVE: It could be that her parents are right. Maybe they're afraid she'll get married early and not finish her education. I suspect that her parents made the same mistake.

BETTY: Her parents might have the wrong idea on going steady. Some think going steady is a guaranteed date and others think it's the next thing to marriage. Some parents get too excited over nothing!

CHUCK: Maybe there was a close family tie with her parents. They are worried for fear they might lose their daughter. She may have trouble *ever* breaking away. Close families are nice, but parents have got to understand that you have to grow up sometime!

JACK: Why go steady? You shut out more than you shut in.

JOE: I think the whole trouble is that her parents aren't too happy about the fellow she is going with.

RUTH: Well, it may be that an older sister had a tragedy — got into real trouble, and the parents think that the younger daughter is heading for the same. In this case, they may be right.

RONNIE: To me there's only one answer: the parents think that going steady is linked right in with marriage. They think this character would be a poor son-in-law. They want their daughter to be well-matched and so they are worried about the situation!

ANN: Sometimes it's not easy for parents to admit that anyone is good enough for their daughter. This fellow may be real nice.

BRUCE: It could be that they met at church, and are both Christians. Maybe the fellow's folks are poor, but *her* parents are well to do with an oil well in Texas. They can't break the "social barrier" by allowing their daughter to go with such a poor guy. They're sure it won't work out.

JACQUE: I think she is probably from a Christian family, but *he* isn't. Her parents don't want her to go with him and weaken her Christian life. But I think she would pay more attention to her parents if they would go about it in the right way — maybe show her what God says about it — not to be "unequally yoked together with unbelievers."

RONNIE: Is that a yoke?

☆ *Fred has bragged to several guys about the number of girls he has kissed.*

QUESTION: WHY HAS FRED DONE THIS?

LARRY: It's common for a guy to brag about how many girls he has kissed. He wants the other guys to think he's a "great lover."

DAVE: Why be a "great lover"?

ANN: He probably felt inferior around the fellows and wanted to show them that he was just as good as they were.

LEO: What's wrong with kissing? It isn't going to kill anyone.

STEVE: A lot of times when a guy isn't a good athlete or can't do other things, he makes up for it by trying to be a hero with the women.

JOE: I'd say that he's just trying to compare notes with the other fellows. He wants to find out what the other fellows are doing because he's not sure of their standards, and he wants to see what they think. He's merely trying to find out what is right or wrong.

SANDRA: Maybe he likes a certain girl but isn't sure about her reputation. He thinks that he can get a line on her by mentioning her name along with the other girls he has supposedly kissed and then watch the reaction of the fellows.

JACK: It could be he's had a rough home life and he just doesn't know any better.

PEGGY: He lets the movies and television programs set a certain standard for him to go by. Everyone's doing it, he thinks, so now he wants to brag that he's doing it too.

RONNIE: He may be too young to know what a kiss really stands for. All he cares about is having people think he's a "man of experience." He will grow out of it. Give him time!

HAL: Sounds to me like he's the kind of guy who is always talking about himself because he's got a blown-up idea of his own importance.

SANDRA: I used to go with a guy like that. All he wanted to talk about was himself and how good he was. What a bum!

☆ *Sharon had been going steady for several months. One night she returned from a date exceptionally late. When her father met her inside the front door and talked to her about it, Sharon resented it, lost her temper, and insulted her father.*

QUESTION: WHAT MAY HAVE CAUSED SHARON TO ACT LIKE THIS?

JOE: She was tired. People do funny things when they're tired. She wasn't herself.

JACQUE: Maybe she felt that it was none of his business. She thought she was old enough to take care of herself.

BOB: It probably means that she had done something she was ashamed of.

BRUCE: I wouldn't be surprised if she has a pretty rough time at home. She probably doesn't get along with her parents on anything. If that's true, then what else could you expect.

GARTH: I bet that for the last three months her parents had gotten down her neck about everything she had been doing. They kept telling her how wrong she was. She couldn't take it any longer, so this caused her to blow her top.

FRANK: I think she had just been arguing with the fellow she was out with. Maybe they just broke off. When her Dad bawled her out, she went to pieces. He should have waited until the next morning.

SANDRA: Maybe they had a good excuse, but her Dad didn't give her a chance to tell what happened. I mean, sometimes parents are too suspicious.

MARY: It could have been that she was a new Christian and she had been witnessing to her boy friend.

ANN: Even if this were the case, I don't think she was wise about the time and place she chose to witness to him. Her Dad may still have had a point.

RONNIE: I think she had a bad temper and acted that way most of the time. I doubt if she was saved. It sounds like someone I know — but it's no one here in this room!

☆ *Although John has some questions in his mind about sex, he doesn't feel free to talk to his Dad about them.*

QUESTION: WHY DOES JOHN FEEL THIS WAY?

LEO: He doesn't feel his Dad knows the answers. I don't think mine does either.

LARRY: I'd say his relationship with his Dad is not too friendly and he doesn't feel free to talk about such things with him. Maybe his Dad gave him the taboo treatment on such things when he was younger.

JACQUE: John is probably embarrassed about the subject and doesn't know how to approach his Dad on it. I think his Dad should sense this, and bring the subject up in the right way.

RONNIE: Maybe sometime before his Dad had embarrassed him by being vulgar about the subject.

DAN: It looks to me like the father is too embarrassed and won't talk about sex to John.

BARBARA: Some kids feel that their parents are too old to understand any of the problems of today's young people. That could be the reason with John.

MARY: Maybe his Dad tells him not to speak or mention sex because he is afraid it might lead John to some kind of wrong actions.

JACK: I'd say that he won't go to his Dad now because he was told to "forget about it" when he wanted to talk with him before.

BILL: At some time in the past his Dad may have presented the subject in a childish manner.

KARIN: It could be that he has gotten the idea that it's bad to even have questions about sex on his mind at all.

☆ *After Ralph has gone out with a girl a few times he can't get along with her.*

QUESTION: WHY DOES RALPH HAVE THIS TROUBLE?

GARTH: Maybe he is taking out girls with whom he

doesn't have too much in common. That is, he's not taking out the girls that would like his type.

SANDRA: It could be he's only going with a girl for his own enjoyment and he never considers showing her a nice time. A girl doesn't like it if she is given the impression that the date is more important to him than she is personally.

HAL: His parents may fight all the time and he doesn't realize he is doing it himself.

BRUCE: Maybe he's trying to push every girl into marriage and they're not ready for anything like that.

DAVE: I think that if a couple doesn't get too serious, it's easier for them to get along.

☆ *On their way home from school several girls were talking about the best age to get married. One of the girls, Mildred, didn't say much. She didn't think she would ever be interested in getting married.*

QUESTION: WHY DOES MILDRED THINK SHE NEVER WANTS TO GET MARRIED?

JOE: She has a career in mind.

LUCILLE: It's likely that her mother had a very difficult time in childbirth, and Mildred has a fear of that same thing; so she isn't interested in marriage. She's afraid of being a wife and mother. According to a psychology course I'm taking, it's possible to feel such a way and yet not be aware of it.

STEVE: On the other hand, she may have a bad complexion and is unattractive, so she has withdrawn and has nothing to do with the fellows.

GWEN: I'd say that her parents are divorced and her mother has told her wild stories about men and marriage. This has given her a real fear of marriage.

BRUCE: Maybe she has already had illegitimate relations with a fellow, and it has affected her emotional life and has caused her to dislike the thought of getting married.

CHUCK: If that's so, it could be she thinks marriage is primarily for sex, and now that she has had this unpleasant experience, she doesn't think marriage is so wonderful.

JACK: It might be that she has seen so many unhappy marriages that she has become discouraged about the possibility of a happy one. Her sister or her own parents might be very unhappily married.

MARY: Maybe she has financial responsibilities with an invalid mother to support.

HAL: I'll bet her father was an alcoholic or something like that and she is afraid that she might get someone like him.

SANDRA: It's altogether possible that she really wants to get married, but because she doesn't have a good personality she is afraid she never will. So she's covering up her real feelings because she doesn't think she has a chance.

☆ *Dick hasn't had any respect for the girls he has dated. But during the past year since going steady with Marilyn, he has been very careful of his conduct on dates.*

QUESTION: WHY HAS DICK CHANGED SO MUCH DUR-
ING THE PAST YEAR?

BOB: It may be that she's a Christian, so he respects her.

RONNIE: He grew up with the idea of getting away with whatever he could. Now he loves this girl and wants to marry her, so his relationship with her is completely different. He doesn't want her to be like the other girls he has gone out with.

JACQUE: Perhaps he's gotten a bad reputation by his past conduct with other girls, and is on his best behavior because he doesn't want to lose her.

JOE: It sounds to me as though he's found the Lord during the past year. That will change a person quicker than anything else.

MARY: He may have found out that he couldn't really care for a girl for whom he had no respect.

CHUCK: You never can tell, he may be afraid of being a bachelor and figures that he had better get on the ball before it's too late!

PEGGY: Do boys worry about not gettin' married, too?

☆ *Frank attends church and young people's meetings nearly every Sunday, but he spends most of his time thinking about sex.*

QUESTION: WHY DOES FRANK HAVE "SEX" ON HIS MIND ALL THE TIME?

BRUCE: It could be a biological reason. We're not all alike.

RONNIE: It's probably his crowd. They talk sex all the time, so he doesn't have a chance to think about anything else.

Leo: What's wrong with thinking about sex?

Bob: Maybe Frank hasn't had a true Christian experience. As a result the Lord hasn't given him real stability in these matters.

Joe: It seems to me the Bible plays an awful big place in this problem. If he isn't in the Word, when the problem comes along he doesn't have anything to put in his mind besides sex.

Jacque: Maybe his parents have never allowed him to date. Furthermore, he's probably ignorant regarding sexual functions of the body, and this is his way of picking up information.

Chuck: I'd say this is a normal thing for a lot of guys. I think every fellow has this problem. That doesn't mean that you shouldn't work on the problem though.

☆ *Unlike some fellows in his group, Sam never tells off-color or dirty stories. However, he does enjoy listening to such stories.*

Question: What might account for Sam's attitude?

Bob: He may have a poor memory and can't remember any jokes!

Garth: Yeah, or maybe he can't tell jokes!

Ben: I imagine he's been brought up in a family where he's heard such stuff and he has no convictions about it.

Carol: He might have convictions about *telling* such stories, but he has no convictions about *listening* to them.

BILL: I'd say he's a follower of the crowd and not a leader.

MARY: Maybe he's afraid if he doesn't listen he will not be popular. All the rest of his gang may do it.

DAVE: If he's a Christian I know what his problem is — he doesn't have victory in his life.

ANN: Possibly he is afraid to ask questions about the things he wants to know concerning sex, and this is the way he is seeking information which he can't get anywhere else. Anyone who has had wholesome teaching about sex isn't so apt to be interested in dirty stories.

JOE: Maybe he's deaf and dumb!

BRUCE: Yeah, he's plenty dumb all right!

☆ *Mel acts more like a girl than he does like a boy.*

QUESTION: WHY DOES HE ACT LIKE THAT?

STEVE: He could be an only child and babied quite a bit. In other words, he is tied to his mother's apron strings. It is possible that, because of this, he doesn't even realize that he acts like a girl.

BOB: Maybe he's not strong and healthy. He may be a brilliant student but lacks physical ability, so he has stuck close to home. He has received a lot of his personality from his mother.

JACQUE: I'd say he has several sisters but no father or brothers. He is always around women.

Hal: His mother may have been divorced when he was only a tiny baby, and he has never had any training except from his mother and women school teachers.

Bruce: Couldn't it be a hormone imbalance? Maybe he needs to see a doctor.

Mary: Perhaps the parents wanted a girl so badly before he was born that they treat him like a girl now.

Leo: Boy, they must be plenty stupid!

Sandra: Sometimes little boys are made to dress like girls and learn to play house and even be the mother.

Ronnie: So what? I used to play house. It doesn't hurt you.

Janice: Yes, but Mel is grown and he's *still* playing house.

Joe: It could be he had a desire to be popular with the opposite sex but he didn't know how, so he tried to act and look like a girl, thinking he would get along better with them then.

Chuck: Maybe he was worried about the war. He wanted to have the easy life the women have while all the fellows are out fighting.

Jacque: What do you mean — "easy life"? You guys have it a lot easier than we do!

☆ *Before Harold and Sue were married they talked a little about raising a family. Sue indicated that she didn't think they ought to be in any hurry about it. After they were married a year or two Harold realized that Sue felt very strongly about not having a family. In fact, it has become a very serious problem in their marriage.*

QUESTION: WHY DOESN'T SUE WANT CHILDREN?

JACQUE: She probably never had any intention of having a family in the first place. She was afraid to tell Harold, however, for fear he wouldn't marry her.

MARY: It may be that she is afraid of childbirth. Her mother probably filled her ear with all kinds of stories about having a baby.

BARBARA: I'd say she doesn't want the responsibility of being tied to the home. Children would put her right there to stay.

JOE: That's selfish. Maybe she hasn't had the experience of a close-knit family relationship. She doesn't know that a family can be fun. There are four children in our family and I wouldn't want it any other way.

SANDRA: I think that maybe she is worried about giving birth to an abnormal baby and doesn't want to take the risk.

BETTY: Maybe she's worried about not knowing how to care for a baby, or how to raise a child — discipline and all of that.

CHUCK: I think she doesn't realize the possibilities of seeing herself reproduced in another life. She may not even be a Christian.

ANN: She may think because of their financial situation they aren't able to give a baby the things it needs.

PEGGY: In all possibility she is not well. If she felt better she might look at it differently.

KARIN: I know a girl who doesn't want to have children. But her trouble is that she's living with her husband's folks and she doesn't want to have a baby until they have a place of their own. I don't blame her at all.

☆ *While chatting with his pastor about the lack of cooperation from Sunday school teachers, the Sunday school superintendent laughingly said, "Well, preacher, I can't get them to do anything. I guess I know them too well. You see, we grew up together."*

QUESTION: WHAT DID THE SUNDAY SCHOOL SUPERINTENDENT MEAN?

MARY: He thought he was a failure and was trying to cover up for it.

RONNIE: Being he had grown up with them and knowing them so well, it is easier for them to turn him down when he asks them to do something.

GARTH: I think it should have been an asset to have grown up with them.

BOB: Sure it could be, but maybe when he was younger he dated some of the girls who are now Sunday school teachers and he gave himself a bad reputation. Even though he is really trying to serve the Lord, the ones he used to date haven't forgotten what he was like.

JACQUE: Yes, he might have lost their respect.

JOE: He may be an immature Christian whose feelings are hurt easily, and as a result he wants to put the blame off on someone else.

☆ *The youth director and his wife had a series of meetings with the young people of their church. They discussed love, courtship and marriage. After the first meeting Joyce went home and said to her mother, "I didn't like that meeting. I don't think they should talk about such things."*

QUESTION: WHAT CAUSED JOYCE TO SAY WHAT SHE DID?

JACQUE: In her home she has never been told about such things and so she thinks it is wrong.

PEGGY: She knew her mother would be pleased to hear that she didn't enjoy it.

FRANK: She probably said it to make her mother think that she was an angel. It was just a cover-up. She was really more interested than she let on.

HAL: Some people have the idea that sex is bad; and she's probably one of them.

MARY: She may not have had any sex problems yet, and so she felt it was wasted time.

SANDRA: Possibly the youth director didn't handle it wisely and it was embarrassing. Some people are too blunt.

DAVE: If they do it right, I think the best place to discuss dating and marriage is with other young people at church.

Youth Talks It Over

2

Dating and Rating

To her younger brother, it seemed that Gloria had washed her hair seven times! "What's the matter with her, Mom?" he asked. "Gloria's been washin' her hair all afternoon!" "Oh no she hasn't," Mother replied. "Besides, she has a date with Don tonight, and she's just trying to look her best."

But Gloria's older sister understood because she had been dating for several years and she knew that dating was "about the most important thing in the world."

Young people look forward to dating with real anticipation. Older people look back and smile as they remember their dates. For dating is fun — wonderful, important fun. It is the time when young people learn to share their interests and time, their activities and ambitions. Actually, the attitudes one develops toward his dates will tend to establish the pattern of his conduct toward the one he marries. Because dating is such a

27

vital part of life, it is important for each Christian to know some facts about dates — facts which will make dating happy and more worthwhile.

READY FOR DATING?

How old is old enough for dating? No one can count the number of birthdays gone by and say just when a person is old enough, for many things work together to make an individual ready for dating.

Family Influences. Parents and their ideas about boy and girl relationships greatly influence the time a young person begins dating. Some parents feel their children should be a certain age before the first date, and discourage boy and girl associations. Other parents are eager for their children to start going out with young people and provide opportunities for boy and girl interests to develop. Then there are the "in-between" parents who just accept dating when it comes!

Mothers and fathers are sometimes more strict with the oldest child — and so the boy or girl who holds this place in the family may be a little more restricted in dating privileges than brothers and sisters who follow.

Social Development. Social readiness for dating comes when a young person is happy and comfortable with other young people. Boys and girls who enjoy working and playing together develop socially earlier than those who find it difficult to mingle happily with the group.

Most churches and schools have many group activities which encourage the easy association of young people. It is important for boys and girls to participate in such activities, for as they have happy times together they are automatically preparing themselves for the friendships which lead to dating.

Conversation skill was made easier for Dennis when the boys' counselor at camp realized how hard it was for the fifteen-year-old boy to talk to other young people.

"Dennis," the counselor explained, "conversation is very much like a game of catch. The game stops if you don't throw the ball back to your playing partner. Conversation stops too, if you say only the necessary 'yes' or 'no'! So try to toss back a question or an idea."

Physical Development. Physical maturity greatly influences the time when all other readiness for dating will come. Wanting to be part of a mixed group, and interest in the opposite sex come as boys and girls develop toward physical maturity. Because girls reach their adult physical maturity about two years earlier than boys, they are usually interested in dating before boys of the same age. This explains why girls are often attracted to boys a few years older than themselves.

READY, BUT NO DATES!

"Oh, I'm old enough," Dotty frets, "and ready too. My problem is, I just don't have any dates."

An especially young person should not worry too much about not having dates, since most boys and girls of the same age are not dating either. Surveys show that the majority of students in high school do not date regularly. So why waste time moping about not dating regularly? This is a good time to make oneself a really interesting person who will be a good dating partner when the time comes.

Remember, to be datable a person must rate well with other young people. That is, he must have qualities which make him enjoyable and interesting. What are some definite things one can do to make himself rate highly with those he wants to date?

RATING A DATE

A good look at you! A good look at yourself will help you know how you rate with others. Answer these questions carefully and you will see yourself much as others see you. Make a note of any way you think your rating can be improved.

How Do I Act?
  — Do I have a friendly smile?
  — Do I listen with interest when someone talks to me?
  — Am I thoughtful about the desires and needs of others?
  — Do I have the Christian quality of honestly liking and being interested in all people?

Pat wondered why she had so few friends. She knew she was attractive, and she was painfully careful to look her best. But in her anxiety to see how people treated her, Pat failed to "lose herself" in friendliness. She was so eager to tell someone about herself she found it difficult to listen with interest when others talked. And in her own words Pat described her attitude when she said, "There are not very many people I like anyway!" Pat had failed to make God's counsel — "A man that hath friends must shew himself friendly" (Proverbs 18:24) — a part of her living!

What Can I Talk About?

— Do I have a hobby I can share in conversation?

— Do I read enough magazine articles, newspapers, books and other articles, so that I can talk with understanding about the world around me?

— Am I able to talk about the message of the Bible and its wonderfully interesting and inspiring characters?

— Do I know the sports program in my school and community well enough to talk about it with accuracy and interest?

— What do I know about cars? Can I recognize makes and models? (Such information is good for a girl to acquire. It keeps conversation from lagging. There are always cars!)

Ever since grade school days Paul has been described as "quiet" and "shy." He made the honor society in high school, and now part of his college expenses are being met by an engineering scholarship. Paul has good clothes and a nicer than average car. However, when he asks for a date he does it abruptly. When he takes a girl out, it is for an evening filled with long silences, broken only by her attempts at conversation, and his short "yes" and "no" answers. After each date Paul wished he knew how to make an evening with a girl comfortable and interesting.

What Can I Do?

— Can I swim, or skate or play a game of tennis?

— Do I know about interesting places in my community?

- Can I build a good sandwich or make a batch of fudge?
- Am I developing my talents?
- Can I enjoy and appreciate simple, everyday fun?

Judy and Marilyn are next door neighbors. They are cute teen-agers, both seventeen. Judy's happy, full of fun and popular too! And Marilyn — she's forever bored wishing for something exciting to do. Dick has the girls figured out quite well. "Judy appreciates anything," he says, "but Marilyn, you could take her to Paris and back and she still wouldn't think she'd had a good time!" Judy's popular because she's learned to enjoy what she's doing.

How Do I Look?

- Am I careful to be well groomed — soap, deodorant, comb and toothbrush used often?
- Am I neat and clever about looking smart in the clothes I have?
- Is my appearance appropriate for a Christian?
- Am I careful to dress suitably for the occasion?

Dressing habits can make or break your dating opportunities! Everyone who knows Dan likes his easy friendliness and his musical ability, but the same people notice his carelessness in dressing. He often comes to church on Sunday morning in an ill fitting sport shirt with no tie. At a recent banquet he did manage to wear a tie, but he was the only one there without a coat. Girls who like Dan for himself, hesitate to go with him for fear of being embarrassed by his appearance.

When you have carefully answered these questions and checked your own abilities and possibilities, you will know some areas in which you wish to improve yourself. So if you are waiting for your dating time, get busy!

Get busy on your self improvement program at home. Talk with the members of your family and develop your conversational ability. Practice doing things for your family. Take responsibility and prove to yourself how dependable and pleasant you can be.

Get busy in your church too. Ask the Lord to help you find ways in which you can serve usefully. Then as you work willingly and enthusiastically in your church group you will become capable as well as interesting.

God has given us clear and definite directions which help us know how to live and work happily with those around us. He has said, ". . . be ye kind one to another, tenderhearted, forgiving one another, . . . And whatsoever ye do in word or deed, do all in the name of the Lord Jesus" (Ephesians 4:32; Colossians 3:17). God gave these guides to living to help in everyday situations. Live by them and your personality will become so attractive that you will be liked by all who know you.

ASKING — AND THE ANSWER

Dates, of course, require an "asking" and an "accepting." It sounds simple, but sometimes it may be rather difficult and awkward. A few easily remembered guides will make the asking more pleasant and natural.

Asking for a date is simpler if the boy realizes he is just giving an invitation, and all invitations should be cordial and definite. So a boy should smile and act in a friendly manner when he asks for a date. He should also be exact and to the point. The girl will like it when her would-be date says, "The Christian film, 'A Greater Challenge' is to be shown at the Richmond Avenue Church Friday night. Would you like to go?" Such an invitation tells the girl "When" and "Where." It helps her to decide whether she can accept the date.

Boys should avoid the question approach, such as, "What are you doing Saturday afternoon?" Maybe the girl isn't doing anything, but she hesitates to say so until she knows what the boy has in mind.

The boy should also be careful to let the girl know where they are to go on the date. It's no fun for either if he arrives in sports clothes with a weiner bake in mind, and finds his date dressed in her Sunday best.

If the girl accepts the date the boy should let her know that he is pleased. Some response like, "Good, I'm glad you can go," is fine.

If the girl refuses the date, it's still the boy's responsibility to be pleasant. Maybe she really wants to go with him, but for some reason she can't explain why it's impossible. The boy can keep the feeling of friendliness between himself and the girl if he tells her, "I'm sorry, but I'll look forward to seeing you some other time."

Accepting or refusing a date should be done with directness. Some girls have been told that "playing hard to get" is a sure way to make boys like them. So a girl who believes such advice, hesitates and acts reluctant to give the boy a prompt answer to his invitation. Most fellows much prefer a straightforward "yes" or "no." Boy and girl friendships grow more smoothly if things are on an honest, easily understood basis.

A girl should remember that when a boy asks her for a date it is a compliment as well as an invitation. The compliment should be appreciated and the invitation requires a clear cut answer. Sometimes the girl knows at the time she's asked that she wants to accept the invitation. Then a "Thank you, I'd like very much to go!" is in order.

But many times the girl needs to check with her parents, or find out if she is involved in some other activity. Most any boy is willing to wait a day for an answer if the girl is honest with him.

Sometimes the girl can't accept the invitation, or for some other reason doesn't want to say "yes." And of course, it is her privilege to refuse the date. However, it is her responsibility to refuse with a "Thank you" and a smile. After all, his next invitation may be the one she'll want to accept.

These dating manners are important, for they are quickly mastered ways in which one can rate highly with friends.

Whom To Date?

First dates usually come from the friendships made in church and school groups. These dates with boys and girls from similar backgrounds have many advantages, for both young people have common interests and mutual friends to help with the fun and the conversation.

However, dates are not necessarily limited to the groups one knows well. It's fun meeting new people at church camps, young people's conventions and inter-school activities. In these friendships, the very difference in background makes the other person interesting and gives both much to talk about.

To a Christian, one part of the date's background and life is vitally important — Is your date a Christian too?

"Why should that matter?" you ask. "He's a grand guy! His father works with my Dad — his family is real nice."

The answer to the question, "Why should it matter?" is one that can be easily answered if it is carefully and prayerfully thought through.

Bob did a lot of thinking before he came to a decision about dating Joy. Some of his thinking was done in school!

"She's pretty and sweet," thought Bob, *"I'd sure like to take her out!"*

He knew that she was a fine talented girl. However, she did not have a vital faith in Christ.

Bob realized that from the girls he dates some day he'll choose the girl he will marry. And he'd read the God-given advice in II Corinthians 6:14, "Be not unequally yoked with unbelievers."

"If I take her out how do I know I won't grow to love her?" Bob asked himself. And so he finally reached a decision. "I'm not going to date girls who aren't Christians," he said. "Then the girl I marry will believe the same things I do!"

Bob is right! He is sure to be more happy if the one he grows to love shares his own faith in Christ. He is being more than wise — he is being obedient to God's will!

Bob had learned an important lesson from Joe, an older boy next door. Last year Joe was a teacher in the junior Sunday school department. Then he started dating

Mary, an attractive girl from a different denominational group. He thought she was saved.

Finally they announced their engagement, then were married.

Bob met Joe recently on the street. "It's good to see you, Bob!" Joe said eagerly. "I sure miss all of the crowd down at the church."

"We miss you, too!" Bob said. "Can't you bring Mary to the young people's meeting tomorrow evening? You know Jim Peterson — he's speaking."

"Sorry, Bob," Joe answered. His smile was gone and he spoke hesitantly. He seemed almost embarrassed. "To tell you the truth, Mary and I — well, we don't go to church much any more. You see, Mary won't come over here to church and I don't like her church because they don't preach the Gospel. Sometimes it gets pretty lonesome, and a little discouraging," he added with an apologetic half laugh.

Bob watched Joe until he disappeared around the corner. *Boy,* he thought, *I'm glad I'm not in his boots. That's one mistake I'm not going to make.*

WHAT TO DO AND WHERE TO GO

Problems of what to do and where to go on dates are not so difficult if the couple are both Christians. Furthermore, no one has as much fun as a Christian. He enjoys himself while on a date, with no regrets afterward.

To sincere believers there is little question about appropriate places to go and things to do. From God's matchless Word we learn, "Whether therefore ye eat, or drink, or whatsoever ye do, do all to the glory of God" (I Corinthians 10:31).

Young people who are not Christians are constantly on the lookout for places where they can go to have a good time. Little do they know that this restless, unavailing search for happiness is the result of the fact that they have never been born again. Happiness is not dependent upon where we are, but rather, upon what we are! If we know Him as our personal Saviour, our sins are forgiven, and He has given us a new nature. Truly life is wonderful and different!

Christian fellows and girls can have a good time almost any place and at any time because they carry their happiness with them — in their heart — it is Christ!

But aren't there some "marginal" places to go — places that may or may not be suitable for Christians? Yes, there do seem to be places like that. But again the Christian couple can make certain by asking these questions: "Would I feel free to take Jesus there?" "By going there will it cause anyone to stumble?" and "Will it help me to develop spiritually?"

Every date should be an occasion when one person inspires another to live closer to the Lord. And yet some couples find it difficult to look each other in the eye, after having acted in a cheap, unwholesome way on a date.

We should never forget that He who died to redeem us is interested in everything we do, in every breath we take!

So a couple can get the most out of every date if they sense the presence of Christ who is with them, remembering, "Trust in the Lord with all thine heart; and lean not to thine own understanding. In all thy ways acknowledge him, and he shall direct thy paths" (Proverbs 3:5, 6).

DATING DECISIONS

It's fun to be asked for a date and it's fun to be accepted. Sharing of good times and experiences with someone you like is a very special kind of fun. But dating is serious business, too! And every young person who dates has problems to face and decisions to make.

Going Steady?

Young people who like each other a lot (or even a little) often ask themselves, "How about going steady?" There are many reasons why "going steady" is an inviting situation.

Helen wanted to go steady. She thought it was a good way to be sure she'd have someone to take her to all the affairs she wanted to attend. Gwen wanted to go steady too, but mostly because so many young couples she knew were doing it. Of course, it is possible for a couple to care so much for each other that they honestly want to spend all of their dating time together.

Sometimes a boy and girl get started going together simply as a matter of convenience — perhaps to finish out a group. After a few happen-so dates the crowd seems to take the couple for granted. Rather than hurt each other's feelings they keep on dating until going together becomes a habit more by accident than by affection. Of course such dating is not a good basis for going steady.

Steady dating limits a person's chances for meeting other interesting boys and girls. One is likely to have a better developed personality and a greater understanding of people if he has had the experience of dating more than one person. And how long does "going steady" last? Some couples find going steady isn't as much fun as they had anticipated. At any rate it may be the part of wisdom to have an understanding that "going steady" may be for any length of time.

Couples who go steady may want to plan many of their dates with a group. Then they will have the opportunity to find out if there are others among their friends whom they would like to know better. One thing is sure — the world is full of wonderful Christian people. Don't miss knowing some of' them!

Petting

Some of the most common questions about dating have to do with petting. "Does everyone pet?" "Is it wrong?" "Must I pet to be popular?" There is not a set of answers to fit all the questions about petting. But young people who know some of the facts are able to face this boy and girl problem more satisfactorily.

What is petting? Petting is love-making between members of the opposite sex. It produces sexual excitement. The ways of petting are many. Any combination of kissing, caressing and bodily nearness is commonly called petting.

In itself, petting is not a complete experience, for in marriage it is normally love-making which precedes the full bodily contact of sexual intercourse. So in marriage the intimacies of petting have a God-planned purpose and become part of a satisfying, rightfully wonderful experience. However, before marriage, heavy petting becomes a real problem, for it gives the powerful stimulation of physical desire which may lead to sinful acts of immorality.

Why do people pet? One might think people pet only because they are deeply in love. In reality, there are many other reasons boys and girls make petting a part of their dates. Some think petting is an expected part of dating, and they are afraid of being different — afraid of not doing the expected thing. Some young people receive very little love from their own family, so petting offers that affection which they need and want, sometimes unconsciously. Boys and girls who have gotten into the habit of petting from some former dating experiences, feel it is the only pattern for dating behavior. Some young people have found the sexual excitement of petting so tempting that they have become absolutely irresponsible and play at petting as a game — a game to be played with any partner available . . . And then there is the engaged couple honestly in love, wanting to express their affection for each other.

How dangerous is petting? No matter what the reasons for petting may be, thinking people agree that the following serious problems and dangers are involved in heavy petting:

- It gives sexual excitement without satisfaction.
- It leaves one with feelings of guilt.
- It sometimes leads to premarital sexual relations with all the tragic problems of unmarried pregnancy.
- One's petting reputation becomes known! It may ruin one's chances to date really fine people. Some adult Christians have found that their work for the Lord has been seriously hindered because

they have an unfortunate reputation from their dating days.

Must I pet to be popular? The popularity that comes with heavy petting does not honor Christ. Neither does it demand respect from others. Genuine popularity is based largely upon friendliness, sincerity and good Christian character. A Christian young person likes to date someone who encourages him spiritually, someone who can do things, someone who is interesting, someone who is sincerely friendly and fun to be with!

Solving a Problem

Ken Wilson's Dad had given him some advice about dating and petting.

"Keep busy, son," he said. "Take your girl to interesting places, tell her how pretty she is — but you'll be wise to have a 'hands off' policy, and not get too involved. Time for that later on."

The advice worked fine until Ken and Barbara had gone steady for several months. "Hands off" just didn't seem practical then.

That's why Ken had stopped by the church to see John Adams, the assistant pastor and youth director. After finally getting around to the topic, Ken asked, "What's wrong with me, Mr. Adams?"

"Nothing's wrong with you, Ken. And nothing is wrong with your Dad's advice either. You've gone steady with Barbara for quite awhile you say, and you like her very much. It's normal for you to want to be close to her and you shouldn't be ashamed of your feelings. They're good healthy feelings. But it's the way you control them that counts. That's what your Dad meant."

"You mean," said Ken, "that it's normal to feel like this, but I'm not supposed to do anything about it?"

"Of course you should do something about it," said Mr. Adams. "Tell Barbara how much you like her. Show how you feel in your thoughtfulness and in wanting to do things together. Get her a little gift now and then. Of course there will be some physical expression of your love, Ken, but then's when the control comes in — when your nearness to Barbara and your thoughts of her become sexually exciting, it's time to move on to another activity. Barbara's a fine girl, and it's your responsibility as a Christian fellow to lead her into a closer fellowship with Christ! Spend your time now in good fun. Getting acquainted sexually must come after marriage. That's the only way you can expect God's blessing on your lives."

Ken was quiet for a moment then said, "Thanks a lot, Mr. Adams. You've helped me. You're absolutely right."

"Just one more word," said Mr. Adams. "It's not my advice, Ken; it's the instruction God gives. And you're not going to have to do this all alone you know! When you get home read these Bible references I've jotted down on this slip of paper. And don't forget, Ken, God's strength for a Christian is waiting, always ready when you need it!"

But Ken didn't wait until he got home to look up the Scripture references. The Bible he carried in the glove compartment of his car was open before he started the motor.

He read Philippians 4:13 and 19, first. "I can do all things through Christ which strengtheneth me . . . But my God shall supply all your need according to his riches in glory by Christ Jesus." Then he read I Corinthians 10:13, "There hath no temptation taken you but such as is common to man: but God is faithful, who will

not suffer you to be tempted above that ye are able;
but will with the temptation also make a way of escape,
that ye may be able to bear it." And then, ". . . Let everyone that nameth the name of Christ depart from iniquity"
(II Timothy 2:19).

Ken's Bible was still open on the front seat as
he headed toward Barbara's house. He felt right! He felt
thankful, too. Thankful for his matchless Christ who
was able to help him — thankful for Barbara's love!

Questions and Answers

When is a boy or girl old enough to start dating?
Dating readiness is not based on how many years you have lived, but on your ability to get along with other young people. Social development as well as physical development determine when you are ready to date. Most boys and girls are dating by the time they are in their middle teens.

What can I do to be popular with others my age?
Every boy or girl can "up" his rating with other young people by being friendly. An honest interest in people around you, a neat appearance, being able to carry on a conversation, and being a consecrated Christian will all work together to make your personality attractive to others.

Why are dates important?
Dating is really an education. As you date you are learning much about different people and different situations. You are also learning much about your own reactions, your likes and dislikes. Dating can be a vital part of personality development, because you gain knowledge and experience from being with others. Dates are important because eventually they may lead, through a process of choice and elimination, to real love.

*Dates in our crowd are always the same old stuff.
We ride around and then have something to eat.
Since we don't dance or go to shows, what is there
to do?*

Use your ingenuity and imagination to think up something different. There are barbecues, picnics, swimming,
tennis, hiking, concerts, ball games, at-home-fun, parties,
church activities, Christian films, song fests, Gospel teams,
and a host of other good times. No one has as many interesting things to do as a Christian!

Should a date be ended with a good-night kiss?
You will have to decide what you want a kiss to mean.
Many young people want to save a kiss for telling that
certain person "you're wonderful"—when that time comes.
A warmly said "Thanks for a grand evening" is a fine
good-night, and it keeps your relationship friendly and
inviting. Casually given kisses leave both boy and girl
with a question mark. *"Does he try to kiss everyone he
takes out?"* she wonders. *Does she kiss everyone she
dates?"* he asks himself.

*When you are tired of going steady how do you
"break off"?*

The best solution is an honest talk about the way you
both feel. From this talk you should attempt to reach
a friendly understanding. If either the boy or the girl
is tired of going steady it is important to break the steady
agreement.

Is it necessary to pet to be popular?
No. Such popularity *is not* lasting or desirable. Real
and satisfying popularity is built on an attractive Christian
personality and friendliness.

The Word of Life

3

A Christian View of Sex

Only a mind reader could have known just how Barry felt as he left the gym Friday afternoon. Up to this time he had been able to justify his way of living, but now he had begun to wonder if he was really being cheated out of something he was entitled to. *"Am I a chump?"* he thought to himself.

In the locker room after football practice, there was usually a lot of talk about girls and dating, especially when the coach wasn't around. Some of the fellows told off-color stories, and a few exchanged accounts of their exploits. It all sounded rather exciting, but he wasn't sure that they had the right answer.

Barry had more respect for girls than some of the fellows did, but during recent months their remarks about his not going out with them and "living it up" had made him wonder if he was a sucker — too "good" to really enjoy life!

47

On many of the streets he noticed giant-sized bill-boards advertising such things as prune juice, picturing girls in scanty bathing suits. When he watched television at home, a glamorous girl with a suggestive quality in her voice sang, "Love Me or Else." Even the news cars were advertised with alluring girls getting in or out of them. Just about everywhere he was reminded of sex.

Should he go along with it, or disregard it, or what? He wasn't sure. Nevertheless, with all this emphasis on sex, he was unduly stimulated much of the time.

Small wonder, then, that when Barry went out with Sue, his favorite date, thoughts of sex were uppermost. They had been going out together for some time, and he could tell that Sue had the same thoughts. It was the way she dressed on occasion and the little things she did that told him. By now he knew that she expected him to kiss her after each date. He liked Sue a great deal and wanted her to know it, but he couldn't feel quite right about the way they were becoming involved. This bothered him. He knew he had to decide for himself whether the thing they were doing was really right. He sensed that both of them were being compelled by emotions which could at some time take control, and carry them he hardly knew where. Their relationship was taking on a pattern, that was certain, and he wasn't convinced that it was the right one.

Dad had been no help whatsoever. When Barry approached him on the subject, he faltered in his speech and acted self-conscious as if Barry had caught him stealing apples from the neighbor's yard. As for asking Mom, it was out of the question. He remembered only too vividly how she had gasped when she found a touch of lipstick on his collar one night after a date with Sue.

His counselor at school was supposed to be available for such discussions, but how would Barry approach him, what would he say? After all, he hadn't done anything wrong — yet! Mostly he wanted to know what was right, and he certainly didn't want to show his ignorance. His own pastor might know the answer, but again the thought of asking such questions was embarrassing. Barry didn't know where to go for advice.

The little reading he had done in physiology class on how the sex organs function had helped somewhat in the area of understanding, but these books hadn't offered him much guidance on how to act.

Barry dropped to the edge of his bed and his glance fell onto the black, leather-bound book on the table by his bedside. It was the Bible his parents had given him for his birthday. He had not read it often. Maybe *it* had some answers to his questions. He picked it up, sprawled on the bed, and began reading — searching. "So God created man in his own image, in the image of God created he him; male and female created he them . . ." It sounded interesting. He would read on.

Barry had, indeed, turned to the most authoritative source for answers to his questions. God who inspired the Bible is the same God who made the marriage of man and woman a part of His creative plan. God's attitude toward sex, as reflected in the Bible, is what Barry and Sue and their whole crowd need to accept, if they are to be happy and well-adjusted.

God has an intense interest in His creatures. He wants men and women to be well-adjusted in every area of life. He desires that courtship and marriage be the means of mutual contentment rather than frustration. By ordaining marriage, God planned that men and women through physical union might share with Him a partnership in -begetting new lives. God alone possesses the power to create, that is, to bring something out of nothing, but through marriage, mating, conception and child-bearing, God permits a man and a woman to be His instruments in creating a new life — an immortal soul! What a wondrous thought! A partnership with God! Sex is a sacred and sobering area of life when seen in Scripture from the viewpoint of God's creative purposes.

How important it is, therefore, for Barry and Sue to know what God says in the Scriptures regarding sex conduct. What more authoritative source could they consult for guidance and help? Here they will find out why God has ordained sex and how He expects men and women to use it. Here they will learn that the same God who warns so severely against the misuse of sex also sympathizes with and understands those who stumble in this area. God knows the importance and the complexity of sex, and in His great providence He gives instruction in His Holy Word.

Unfortunately, many people have mistaken ideas regarding what the Scripture teaches. Some believe that the Bible bans and taboos relations between the sexes as "nasty" or as sinful. Not a few frustrated old spinsters have been of the opinion that sexual intercourse was the original sin. "That's the way Adam and Eve sinned," they mutter through pursed lips, "and God meant for them to be innocent and pure all their lives."

Such talk spreads an untruth which has no foundation in Scripture. God created Adam and Eve and placed them in a beautiful garden with the command, "Of every tree of the garden thou mayest freely eat: but of the tree of the knowledge of good and evil, thou shalt not eat of it: for in the day that thou eatest thereof thou shalt surely die" (Genesis 2:16, 17). The original sin of Adam and Eve was clearly disobedience to God's command by eating of the forbidden tree. The fact of their union in marriage had nothing whatever to do with it. In fact, sex could not have been connected with sin because marriage was instituted by God before Adam and Eve fell into sin (Genesis 1:28).

Psalm 51:5, ". . . in sin did my mother conceive me," is another verse often erroneously interpreted. This verse, when considered in context, has no reference at all to the sex act. It simply points to a fact underlying all of human existence, that since Adam, human nature has shown a continuous tendency to sin, and that we are all born with sinful natures inherited from the original man and woman.

These and other misconceptions of Scriptural teachings are frequently the inventions of people who have little or no spiritual insight into the meaning of the Bible, because they have never been born again and have not received spiritual discernment. A correct understanding of the Bible is the result of diligent study graced by the inner teaching of the Holy Spirit. Even Christians can slip into false ideas, if they do not continually give themselves to searching the Scripture under the guidance of the Holy Spirit.

Actually the Bible has many wonderful things to say about man's relation to woman. It states simply and beautifully that "God created man in his own image, in the image of God created he him: male and female created he them. And God blessed them, and God said unto them, Be fruitful, and multiply, and replenish the earth . . ." (Genesis 1:27, 28). God created man and woman in two complementary sexes and ordained marriage both as a source of blessing and enjoyment and as the means of populating the earth. God, by His holy will and purpose, is intimately bound into the institution of marriage from the very start, and He has promised to add His blessing to the sacred union of the man and woman whom He created in His own image.

God knew that it was not good for man to be alone (Genesis 2:18), so He joined him to "an help meet," so that they might cleave together and become one flesh (Genesis 2:24). The first miracle Jesus performed was at a wedding and by doing so He put His hand of blessing upon the marriage relationship (John 2). How mysterious and marvelous is the union of two personalities in marriage! God ordained it, and good it is for all who are thus truly joined by God.

Great responsibility lies with the man. Husbands are told, " . . . love your wives, even as Christ also loved the church and gave himself for it . . . So ought men to love their wives as their own bodies. He that loveth his wife loveth himself" (Ephesians 5:25, 28). The Holy Spirit compares the love a man holds for his wife with the love that Christ gives to those who are members of His church. It is the man's privilege to satisfy the emotional, physical and spiritual needs of his wife, even as Christ meets the needs of all who believe in Him. Surely love on this plane would satisfy any man or woman!

This does not mean that marriage is necessarily right for everyone. To some has been given the gift of singleness that they may serve the Lord in that capacity (I Corinthians 7). The most important thing, of course, is to be in the will of God, whether married or single. Everyone must determine this for himself before the Lord. In selecting a mate, Christians must remember the command of the Lord not to be "unequally yoked together with unbelievers" (II Corinthians 6:14), because complete harmony is impossible on any level when only one of the partners has been born again.

Above all, God's choicest blessing rests upon the marriage of two Christians who are walking with the Lord and enjoying His richest gifts. "Marriage is honourable in all, and the bed undefiled" (Hebrews 13:4), states the writer of Hebrews under the inspiration of the Holy Spirit. The concept of the relationship of man and woman in Christian marriage is the most lofty and challenging that can be imagined.

On the other hand, however, the Bible warns decidedly against the abuse of sex. Unless we have the Bible, we have no chart to guide us through the rough waters of confusion and ignorance.

Fornication, adultery and every other form of illegal sexual union are prohibited time and time again in God's Word. From God's point of view, sexual union is legitimate only within the bond of marriage, for this is the way He ordained it. From man's point of view, it is only within marriage that sexual union can bring peace and full satisfaction. Outside of marriage, frustration, guilt feelings and loss of self-respect result. Promiscuity before marriage only serves to separate two young people who might otherwise have gone on to a beautiful marriage, because they could not face each other with respect after having abused that which God has reserved for husband and wife.

Tom and Marilyn never stopped to think of the consequences as they became intimate in a parked car on a side road. They were beyond thinking. But in the weeks and months that followed, they knew they had sinned, and their shame drove a wedge between them. Wrong acts carry within themselves their own punishment. If they had really cared for each other, Tom and Marilyn would have restrained their emotions which led to the wrongful act.

The Scripture warns, "Flee fornication. Every sin that a man doeth is without the body; but he that committeth fornication sinneth against his own body. What? Know ye not that your body is the temple of the Holy Ghost which is in you, which ye have of God, and ye are not your own? For ye are bought with a price: therefore glorify God in your body, and in your spirit, which are God's" (I Corinthians 6:18-20). Our bodies are the members of Jesus Christ and the temples of the Holy Spirit, if we are Christians. We belong to Him and not to ourselves. What an inspiring motive for turning over to Him all of our emotions, thoughts and actions for His purification and blessing.

All young people who are confused about sex conduct and other important issues in life will find their answer by receiving Christ as Saviour and Lord. He is the center of the happy life. Settling things with Christ is like centering a phonograph record on the turntable; only then will the music play correctly. When

Christ is the center of one's life, all other things, including sex, fall into place.

Although sex is definitely an important part of marriage, it is not to be exalted out of proportion. The sharing of dreams and disappointments, comforting in the hour of need, and having mutual interests, are also of vital importance. Marriage is a love companionship, it is parenthood, it is worshiping and fellowshiping together in Christ.

Once a young person believes in Christ and gives Him full control of his life, then life is exciting — satisfying. There is nothing more beautiful than life as planned by God, and lived in the love of His Son!

Questions and Answers

Does the Bible encourage marriage?

God's Word places considerable emphasis on marriage. Through Adam and Eve, His command to the human race is, "Be fruitful, and 'multiply, and replenish the earth" (Genesis 1:28).

It is also evident from the Scriptures that not all people should marry (I Corinthians 7). Happiness is not dependent upon marriage, but rather, upon one's devotion to the Lord Jesus Christ.

Does God speak of sex as sin?

No, except as it is wrongly used, that is, fornication and adultery — sexual relations outside the bond of marriage. I Corinthians 6; Exodus 20.

Does the unpardonable sin refer to illicit sex relations?

No. In Matthew 12:31 we read, "Wherefore I say unto you, all manner of sin and blasphemy shall be forgiven unto men: but the blasphemy against the Holy Ghost shall not be forgiven unto men." In the preceding verses of Scripture the Pharisees criticized Jesus, saying that He was casting out evil spirits by the power of Satan.

Then Jesus warned them that all kinds of sin and unbelief could be forgiven if one would repent, but that there was one sin which would never be forgiven: attributing the work of the Holy Spirit to the Devil.

The Holy Spirit's glorious ministry among men is to magnify the person and work of the Lord Jesus Christ. If this ministry is persistently ridiculed and rejected, God has no remaining way to save men.

Were all of the great Bible characters married?
Some Bible characters were married, but others were not. For example, Abraham, Moses and Peter were married, but Paul and the Lord Jesus Christ, Himself, were not.

What significance has the Bible quotation, "Be ye not unequally yoked together with unbelievers"?
Believers in Christ are instructed not to be unequally yoked together with those who do not know Christ as their personal Saviour.

Being yoked together surely includes marriage. But undoubtedly it encompasses many other relationships in which common goals, efforts and activities are concerned.

4

Looking Toward Marriage

The last strains of the organ had long since ceased echoing; the last kisses, even some anonymous ones, had left their impressions on the bride's glowing cheeks. The young hopefuls, starry-eyed, had raced through the rattling rain of rice to the waiting car which hummed away to its tin-can accompaniment. Now the crowd was left behind, some solemn, some even tearful, but most — especially the younger ones — wistful and almost envious.

The glances of Janet and her mother met and held as they sat in the back seat of their car. "Oh, Mother," said Janet, "wasn't it just divine? Just think, for them it's all over!"

"Or just beginning," thought the mother. "I've always wondered," she remarked, "how those two happened to choose each other! Kathy's such a shy, sensitive little thing, and Bruce is so aggressive and . . ."

"Oh, Mom! How could you ever think such a thing as that?" interrupted Janet, honestly indignant.

"Bruce and Kathy are in love, really in love; certainly that's reason enough!" — which seemed to Janet a complete answer to her mother's question. To her generation "love" had become the sole requisite for a proper and suitable marriage.

But is love all that is needed to make a marriage happy? And just what is love? Everyone has ideas about "How love feels," or "How love makes you act," but to define or explain it is not so easy. However, since love for another brings us to marriage, and continuing love makes the marriage successful, it is surely important to seek for an understanding of the why's and how's of this deep emotion.

DIFFERENCES IN LOVE

Some love is the strong and sure foundation on which a fine marriage can be built, while another form of love may be doubtful, an unsafe beginning for married happiness. What causes these differences?

Love differs because each individual is a different kind of person; also people are attracted to each other for many different reasons. So the kind of love which grows between a man and woman is influenced by the kind of people they are and the attraction which brought the two together.

— Sympathy for another,
— Loneliness,
— A driving desire for marriage,
— An unhappy situation at home,
— A recent failure or disappointment,
— Meeting a person who is "just like" a loved one,

are some of the reasons why people may be drawn into

marriage. The love which grows from such beginnings may at first seem real. But it is not strong enough to be the safe foundation for a permanently successful marriage. Most of these reasons stem from self-centered desires, loving another because that person seems to supply something which is lacking in one's own life.

However, when one discovers in another such things as common interests, mutual ambitions, devotion to Christ, and a similar background, love has much to make it grow strong, strong enough for marriage. This sturdy, lasting love is overwhelmingly interested in the other person. Making the other one happy becomes more and more important.

   — Sharing ideals and dreams,
     — Working and playing together,
       — Sharing spiritual challenges,
        — Willingly working out differences,
          — Eagerly looking forward to establishing a Christian home and family,

are all characteristics of the love which will grow stronger and deeper with the passing years.

God's Standards of Love

An evaluation of love may be made by reading the inspired thirteenth chapter of First Corinthians. Following are a few pointed phrases: "Love endures long and is kind; love is not jealous; love is not out for display; it is not conceited or unmannerly; it is neither self-seeking not irritable; it takes no pleasure in injustice, has unquenchable faith, endures without limit" (Berkeley Version).

Donna was a student at a well-known college. Though undoubtedly a Christian, she was so lacking in the graces shown in this thirteenth chapter, that she neither showed nor attracted love. In June, just before she went home, the Dean of Women said to her, "My dear, I wish you would promise me one thing; every day this summer read the thirteenth chapter of I Corinthians." Donna promised. In the fall, when she returned, her personality had been radiantly transformed!

Like Donna, we would do well to examine our love in the light of God's standards. But even if we felt reasonably satisfied with the quality of our love, these are not the only requirements for a happy marriage. Loving the right person is important too!

THE RIGHT PERSON TO LOVE

One often hears the statement, "Love is blind." And it is true that an individual clearly sees the fine qualities of the loved one, but often blindly ignores the equally apparent faults. It is good insurance for happiness in marriage to love with both eyes open, for the fact is that *loving a person does not change his basic personality*. Patterns of behavior, character traits and the attitudes a person has before marriage will continue after marriage. This quality of "staying the same" *helps* in choosing a marriage partner, for people who agree and have the same attitudes toward life now, will no doubt, feel much the same in later years.

Christian young people are fortunate when it comes to choosing a life partner, for God has promised guidance concerning whom a Christian should marry. He will never permit any person to have His second best — provided, of course, that the person earnestly seeks God's will.

> God knows, He loves, He cares;
> Nothing this truth can dim,
> He gives His very best to those
> Who leave the choice to Him.

A CHRISTIAN

The prophet Amos asked, "Can two walk together except they be agreed?" And the truth implied by this question is as psychologically sound today as it was when Amos lived, thousands of years ago. Agreement on basic issues greatly increases a couple's chance for a successful marriage. The New Testament command is, "Be not unequally yoked with unbelievers." This makes it clear and definite, that, if one is a Christian, he should know without a doubt that the right one for him must be a Christian also! God's blessings follow obedience to His commands.

THE RIGHT CHRISTIAN

Almost every Christian young person knows other Christians near his own age. How can one know which is the right one to love? First of all, we know that God is interested in each individual, for through his belief in Christ, he is part of God's family! He fully understands how important it is for His own to choose the right partner for life — and He knows just who it should be. So, we should prayerfully seek His wisdom and His guidance. God's unfailing Word promises, "The Lord shall guide thee continually . . . He will be our guide even unto death" (Isaiah 58:11; Psalm 18:14).

Knowing the qualities which make a good marriage-partner will help you to recognize God's guidance. Studies of numerous happy marriages show that the right person for you will be:

— someone you enjoy being with;
— someone whose character and personality you admire;
— a person with common interests and mutual ambitions;
— a person whose social and cultural background is similar to yours;
— someone whose denominational beliefs are near enough your own so there will be no disagreement over church membership;
— someone whose standard of living will be easy for you to accept;
— an individual whose intellectual and educational levels will be near enough your own to assure you the joy of companionship in shared understandings.

And most vitally important, that right one for you should share your consecration to Christ and your spiritual devotion. In other words, the right Christian for you will be someone who is "going your way" with Christ!

Amy and Paul had experienced a long friendship, deepening into love during his seminary years. While Paul studied, Amy worked in the school office. They looked forward to a June wedding following Paul's graduation. At the beginning of their engagement there had been much discussion about his deep interest in foreign missions, and his application was actually under consideration. But Paul became uneasy. Amy had twice asked about looking at the new housing development just north of town. She even mentioned the amount of the down payment. Paul believed that he had a definite call to South America, but he was beginning to feel that Amy really wanted to remain here at home. Paul wondered how he had become entangled by such a problem. It could have been avoided by making sure, in the beginning, that Amy and he had the same ambition — the same life-goal.

Occasionally, there are marriages which seem happy when the husband and wife have completely unlike backgrounds and widely separated interests, but such marriages are the rare exception rather than the rule. Marriage authorities who have analyzed thousands of cases, agree that similarities in cultural backgrounds are desirable materials for building a successful marriage.

YOU'LL HAVE THREE FAMILIES

As you look toward marriage you realize you will soon be part of three families — the family you grew up in — the family you'll marry into — and the new family your marriage will establish. Suddenly having three families instead of one can be complicated unless you and the one you are to marry have prepared yourselves for the family changes which come with marriage.

YOUR FAMILY

First of all, getting married will separate you from your own family — and this is right. Your ability to accept this change with confidence is an indication that you are ready for marriage. Christ spoke of the oneness of husband and wife when He said, "For this cause shall a man *leave* father and mother, and shall *cleave* to his wife."

Just how separated you'll be from your family will depend on your emotional maturity as well as how far away from home you'll be living. There is danger in being too closely tied emotionally to one's parents, for the dependent feelings of childhood will cause trouble if they continue after marriage. However, it is important to keep wholesome, mature family ties strong, for there is satisfaction and happiness in being a part of a larger family group. The family ties you establish in early marriage will help your children have a happy time with their "Grandpas" and "Grandmas."

THE FAMILY YOU MARRY INTO

The marriage which takes you apart from your own family also takes you nearer to the family of the one you marry. His folks will be your folks, and your folks will be his folks! Often this is a happy and rewarding time for all concerned. Families gain a son or daughter, and each of the newly married gets a new family. And when two people get married everyone seems to become someone's "in-law"!

Tensions can be avoided by getting to know both families before marriage. Of course, you'll want to talk about your families. Discussion is fine, but it is not enough, for although you want to be honest it's hard to be entirely objective about your own family. So, before marriage, if distances are not too great, visits should be made in both directions.

In fact, it would be wise for these visits to take place even before the engagement. Then if you find the family is unacceptable you can break away from the relationship without too much difficulty. If you have become engaged and then find the family situation undesirable, you still have time to make the necessary break before it is too late. Whether we like it or not, marrying a person is to a great extent marrying his or her family also.

Family visits will show you the background which produced the one you love. Attitudes, spiritual interests, as well as economic, social and educational levels found in the family will be important. Remember the one you love will be much like the family he came from.

But don't expect both families to be too nearly alike. Both of you will have to accept with Christian tolerance and understanding certain personality differences and varieties in living patterns. Talk together about these differences and prayerfully try to reconcile yourself to them before marriage. Then you will be able to start a happier new home for the family which will be yours.

MOTHERS AND DADS IN YOUR MARRIAGE

Of course every thoughtful parent is vitally interested in his son's and daughter's life partner. At times it may seem that mother and dad don't understand the problems of dating and marriage, and that they interfere too often. Sincere young people, however, cannot afford to overlook the important role parents play in their marriages. This is especially true if mother and dad are devoted Christians. Studies such as those by E. W. Burgess and L. S. Cottrell reveal that marriages having the sanction of parents are more likely to succeed than those that do not. True, there are exceptions, but the findings of such research are important to you.

Why is it so necessary to have the counsel and cooperation of parents? Naturally, parents are more mature and experienced than their children. They may be more objective and frank. They know their sons and daughters well and can help them during times when an engagement may hit a "snag." They are of inestimable help in making arrangements for the wedding and in speaking a good word about the prospective marriage. Should serious difficulties arise after marriage, parents could help avert a real tragedy.

Children need grandparents, and young couples contemplating marriage should strive to foster good relationships with their mothers and dads. But most important of all, couples need the prayers of their parents. Life is not a series of chances. Rather, life is moulded and modified daily through prayer. And parents as well as grandparents can bring untold blessing upon their loved ones!

So if you have one eye on the altar, don't overlook the mothers and dads in your marriage. They just may turn out to be V.I.P.'s — the most important people in your life!

A Christian Home for Your Family

Planning for the home and family is a wonderful part of looking toward marriage. "Where shall we live?" "What furniture can we afford?" "Blue or green walls?" "How many children?" — are all questions of thrilling importance. The Christian couple looking forward toward a life together find a happy challenge in planning how their home can be a Christ-centered background for their future family.

Your Church —

A well-established Christian family should have a church home. So, *before* marriage, talk about your church membership. You'll also want to take an active part in your church, with specific duties which will add value to your Christian life and become a worthwhile example for the children who will some day be watching you. Any church worth your membership is also deserving of your time and talent.

Your Home —

By the phrase, "family worship," is visualized an open Bible and heads bowed in prayer. Such worship must be a daily part of the Christian family life, for there is no better way to establish God the Father, and His Son Jesus Christ, as the security and salvation for each member. "Just two" is enough for family worship, so plan to start this all important part of your family life as soon as you are married.

Family Fun —

Let there be much laughter in the home, for laughter is good medicine. Encourage funny stories, jokes, puns and jolly simple games in which the whole family can participate. A developed sense of humor will help to eliminate petty bickering and restore strained relations to their proper perspective. "A merry heart doeth good like a medicine" (Proverbs 17:22).

Family Reading —

Since what you read will influence what you think and how you act, make the reading material in your home reflect your Christian ideals. Deciding on desirable books and periodicals will be an interesting way to spend some time before marriage. Your pastor will be glad to recommend Christian books and magazines for you to consider.

Decisions in the Home —

A Christian home should be managed democratically. So with the husband as the head and moderator, let discussion lead the way to decisions which are mutually acceptable.

Those Around You —

The responsibility of the Christian home does not stop with the family itself, so plan and pray that your home will maintain a clear testimony for Christ to your neighbors as well as to your families and friends. And about your friends — you will need Christian friends for they will help strengthen your Christian lives and you will help strengthen theirs as you have fellowship together. Friends who do not have the same spiritual standards make it hard for you to develop into faithful and fruitful Christians.

A secure and happy home will be the result of your planning if. you decide before marriage — "as for me and my house we will serve the Lord!" (Joshua 24:15).

READINESS FOR MARRIAGE

Really happy marriages are made by people who are ready for marriage. And being ready means more than loving the right person. It also means being mature enough for marriage. This maturity does not come at any special age, but statistics show that teen-age people are rarely ready to accept the responsibilities of married life.

Helen and Phil were both nineteen. They met at a church camp a year ago and then they attended the same college. Being together, doing the same things and planning for the future was wonderful fun for these two young people, for they loved each other and were interested in the same kind of life. Phil said, "Let's get married. If we both work as we do now, and skimp a little, we'll still be able to finish school." At first Helen agreed with Phil. But the more she thought about cooking and dish washing, keeping their clothes washed and ironed, cleaning an apartment — and maybe a baby, — the more attractive seemed the care-free, fun-life which they already had.

Helen and Phil might better decide to wait awhile. True, they may have reached their physical maturity, but the more slowly developed emotional maturity which enables one to accept all phases of life, is needed for a happy and secure marriage.

The person who is able to get along well with himself and others and confidently accepts many kinds of situations shows emotional readiness for marriage. Such a person is able to

— be realistic,
　— accept situations as they exist,
　　— make decisions,
　　　— cooperate well,
　　　　— love someone besides himself,
　　　　　— accept frustrations and disappointments.

These traits in an individual show his suitability as well as his readiness for marriage.

The emotionally mature person is also able to recognize that sometimes it is wise to postpone present satisfactions for the greater future good. This is an important part of being grown up enough for marriage, for there is often need for waiting or saving ahead.

For three months Molly and David went without extra magazines, candy, nonessential clothing, or any eating away from home. They wanted to be able to take a trip to Yellowstone when vacation time came, and with a bit saved here and there they'll be able to make their vacation plan into a reality.

The immature person finds this type of postponement difficult, but the ability to forego some present good for a greater future gain increases with emotional maturity.

As someone has well said, "Nothing worthwhile has ever been achieved that has not been the product of some form of resolute self-denial." Parents, who for themselves have already learned self-control will later be able to teach their children. As George Eliot expressed it, "Life is a succession of choices; we cannot often have this *and* that, but this *or* that."

SPIRITUAL MATURITY

Spiritual maturity is a vital part of marriage readiness, for with marriage comes the thrilling and happy, but serious responsibility of establishing a Christian home. To be ready for marriage spiritually means first of all that you have accepted Christ, God's Son, as your Saviour. It also means that you are eager to make your life count for Christ in consecrated everyday living.

There is no greater opportunity for Christian living than through the home, and if you are fitted for this opportunity you will be willing to: (1) make church attendance a part of your family life; (2) establish family worship in your home; (3) make your home a consistent testimony for Christ; (4) let Christian standards regulate your family relationships. The Christian young person who is spiritually ready for marriage agrees with God's Word when it says, "Except the Lord build the house, they labour in vain that build it" (Psalm 127:1).

One of the most important qualities which a person can bring to marriage is deep spirituality. Spiritual understanding and discernment are always necessary. But they are especially important in times of adversity, illness and sorrow, all of which are certain to become a part of every marriage. At times like these, the practice of daily united prayer and Bible reading, if already established, will prove an unfailing bulwark of strength and comfort.

SEX IN MARRIAGE

Being ready for marriage also means having a reassuring knowledge about sex. The Christian young person can look frankly at this aspect of marriage with the happy realization that God created man and woman for each other . . . and that sexual relationships between husband and wife have God's blessing.

Billy Graham, the noted evangelist, says in his book, *Peace With God*, that "sex is the act by which all life on this earth is created and it should be the most satisfying, the most wonderful, the most meaningful of all human experiences." God's Word gives dignity and rightness to the exquisite intimacies of marriage when it says ". . . rejoice with the wife of thy youth . . ." And again, "Marriage is honorable in all and the bed undefiled . . ." (Proverbs 5:18 and Hebrews 13:4).

An important part of being sexually ready to marry is being happily willing to accept the children who may come. Children are the God-planned result of married love, truly "a heritage of the Lord"! The couple who are blessed with children should find great happiness and satisfaction in having fulfilled God's purpose in marriage — the making of a family. If a person is not ready for the demanding responsibilities created by a baby's cry, or the sweet rewarding joy of a tiny one's first smile, marriage should wait. Whether planned for or not, babies have a way of coming, and of becoming part of the family!

As young people look toward marriage they sometimes wonder about statements they've heard concerning sex.

Jim asks, "I've heard that married people often have a lot of sexual adjustments to make before they are really happy. Is this true?" Any new relationship calls for some adjustments, but sexual adjustments are usually minor, especially if both young people are loving, considerate Christians, concerned with making the other one happy in sex relationship. A premarital physical examination by a competent physician may be a wise assurance of physical readiness for happy sexual adjustments.

The one you marry will not have the same sexual desires, capacities and attitudes that you have. No two people are perfectly adjusted, simply because people are not perfect beings. Not only are there significant differences in sex drives and responses between male and female; there are also differences from person to person. So if you're expecting perfection in your marriage, you are bound to meet with some disappointment. But if you enter marriage desirous of making the necessary adjustments even though there are differences, you will undoubtedly be very happy.

Linda worries, "If a person does have serious trouble with marriage adjustments what can be done?" The couple should seek the advice of their physician or a qualified marriage counselor. Such professional help will usually result in a happy solution of the difficulty.

Martha wonders, "Grandmother tells me sex in marriage is only for the purpose of having a family. Does the Bible say that?" Of course, sexual relations are part of God's plan for having children, but He has also made the complete oneness of marriage to be an expression of love. The Bible teaches the wife and husband are for the joy of one another as it advises the husband to "rejoice with thy wife . . ." (Proverbs 5:18).

The ability to come to your loved one with thoughtful, loving tenderness is an important part of sexual readiness. Such an approach to this lovely part of marriage will build a sure foundation for lasting and growing joys in married love.

Being emotionally, spiritually and sexually ready for marriage is important, but even then no two people are ready for marriage unless they know each other well. The better they know each other, the better their chances for a successful marriage. Records show that without doubt, couples who marry after a long acquaintance are happier and have fewer problems than couples who marry on impulse. This is what makes the waiting time so important.

GETTING BETTER ACQUAINTED

Most couples who are seriously looking toward marriage reveal their intentions by happily announcing their engagement. Such an exciting time! The girl is thrilled and proud as she shows her ring — the young man is thrilled too, as he receives the congratulations. What a deep sense of joy and satisfaction! It's the knowledge of both being Christians, belonging to another — and having everyone know you belong — that makes being engaged such a completely happy time.

It is also an *important* time, with weeks and months of opportunity to prepare for marriage. During this period the young couple should become better acquainted, each with the other's personality and ideas. It is the right time for "his" ideas and "her" ideas to be discussed, perhaps changed a bit and finally fused until they become "their" ideas. This does not happen automatically for it takes understanding and patience, as well as love, and much discussion to see the other's viewpoint. But out of this "give and take" of ideas, arises the strength of two people now in accord.

Agreement and understanding develop as the young couple talk and plan together. Before their engagement such subjects as money management, housing and child raising were not even mildly interesting as topics of conversation. But after engagement they become superlatively interesting and vitally important, for they are an integral part of the marriage-to-be. Many times differences of opinion and even disagreements will arise as the engaged couple get better acquainted. This is no handicap, for every difference discovered and worked out beforehand to a mutually satisfactory solution, is one less hurdle to take after marriage.

Kay and Glenn, who were to be married soon, recently visited her married sister. It was fun seeing Jane and her husband, but little Timmy, their four-year-old, was impossible. He interrupted every conversation and demanded constant attention. On the way home Kay and Glenn talked about Timmy and as they talked they realized they had entirely different views on child training. Kay and Glenn want a family, and they will be wise to reach at least a measure of agreement concerning their ideas of child training.

LOVE-MAKING BEFORE MARRIAGE

Some young people become so involved with physical love-making, that they miss out on the fine "getting-to-know-each-other" opportunities of the engagement period. This is unfortunate, if not actually dangerous; unfortunate, since young people who center their activities entirely around love-making, miss knowing each other as interesting people to be enjoyed in varied situations (they also miss out on exchanges of ideas which make many marriage adjustments easier); dangerous also, because the intense desires which accompany constant love-making bring the engaged couple to the point of asking, "Since we belong to each other now — and since we'll be married soon — why wait?"

"Why wait?" is a question with definite answers—answers given by God as well as the society in which we live.

God, who made us, commands that *all* sexual relationships be saved for marriage. He knows that our bodies and minds need the security of knowing we fully belong for life to the other person if the sexual expression of love is to have its full meaning and beauty. God knows that the children who may come because of two people giving themselves completely to each other, will need the loving care of a father and a mother, so God has given His blessing to such a union only within the family situation of marriage. As for sexual intimacy outside of marriage — God calls it *sin*. Christ left no room for doubt or wondering when He said, "Thou shalt not commit adultery" (Matthew 5:27).

It is not only God who says "Wait," but also the society in which we live. The laws and the moral standards of our society make sexual contacts before marriage unacceptable. The person who is discovered disregarding these standards of moral behavior is subjected to much disapproval and loss of respect, to say the least. The greatest of all wedding gifts that any man and woman can give each other is their purity!

Waiting pays dividends of happiness! Waiting is not always easy, even for fine Christian young people. But God's promise for "help in time of temptation" (I Corinthians 10:13) and His assurance for strength equal to the need (Philippians 4:13) make it possible to put aside this temptation for the reaping of the far greater reward that comes from having waited. Those who wait are richly rewarded. Young people who come to marriage with chaste bodies have the beautiful experience of giving themselves, fresh and untouched, to the one they love. Such sexual relationships have the tenderness and ecstasy which make married love one of the most beautiful of all human experiences.

Couples who don't wait are sorry. Sexual relations before marriage are entirely different. The individuals involved must of necessity be watchful and fearful —

afraid of being found out. The shabby, uncomfortable surroundings of a cheap motel or a parked car turn this experience, which in God's setting of marriage is indescribably lovely, into an experiment with damaging reactions.

Many different results, none of them good, come to couples who do not wait sexually for marriage. They feel cheated, for now they have nothing excitingly new and wonderful to look forward to in marriage. They feel disappointed, for their experience together was not as satisfactory or enjoyable as they anticipated. They wonder now if they really want to get married after all. They feel ashamed. Secretly each blames the other for permitting such an experience to take place. Many couples who imagine that waiting would lessen their love find that to the contrary, not waiting has lessened their sex desire. Unmarried pregnancy is also a possibility which must be faced by those young people who do not wait, and there is no way in which such an experience can be lived through without great and permanent scars.

The frustrations associated with waiting are sometimes difficult. Yet, because purity is *right*, the waiting is well rewarded all through life!

Sylvia is a lovely Christian girl. She and twenty-two-year-old Ted have been engaged for a year. Because they are both in school, their marriage date has not been set. Their times together recently have been tense, often they have been irritable with each other. Ted feels that waiting so long for the complete happiness of marriage is piling up frustrations which are ruining their relationship. "Would breaking over the line occasionally ease the tension between us and give us back our feeling of happy comradeship?" Ted wonders.

Authorities answer Ted with finality. The frustrations which attend long waiting are sometimes very real, but they are frustrations based on doing what is *right*. The rightness of the cause for the frustration largely compensates for any resulting unhappiness. "Breaking over the line," as Ted expressed it, or going ahead with sexual relations before marriage, would not in any way solve the problem. It would only add a new problem to an already tense situation. And this new problem would be based on having done the *wrong* thing. Consequently, the results would be much more damaging and the sense of guilt would cling. Ted and Sylvia found waiting difficult, but they would have found not waiting even more difficult.

"Why wait?" is a question with a clear answer. Waiting is the only way a couple can have God's richest blessings, to have the approval of society, yourself and the one you love. Waiting is the only way to know the true beauty of God's plan for married oneness.

MONEY — AND YOUR MARRIAGE

Looking toward marriage also means taking a careful and honest look into the pocketbook. The often repeated, "Two can live as cheaply as one," just isn't true! Married or single, each person must eat, must have a place to live and clothing to wear. Without adequate money for these essentials, adjustments to marriage become dangerously difficult. For this reason a certain degree of financial security is necessary for a good start.

No one can tell the exact amount of money which will fulfill your own need of financial security. It will depend partly on how much each of you has been accustomed to, and how much you each feel you must have after marriage. However, thoughtful planning and talking things over before marriage will help to determine approximately how much money you will need to meet your joint standard of living. If these planning times are to be practical, both must be frank about their incomes, their obligations and their desires.

Nancy and Don had been making careful plans for their marriage during the eight months they had been engaged. They had even worked out a budget for their first year together. But now Nancy felt hurt and puzzled, for Don wanted to set the wedding date three months later than they had planned. At last Don frankly told Nancy that he couldn't afford to get married any sooner for he was using the money they would need for rent, in repaying his uncle from whom he had borrowed money to finish his last two years at the University.

"Certainly we can work it out someway," Nancy argued. But when they figured it out in black and white Nancy could see how much better it was to wait. She did wish that Don had told her about this obligation months sooner.

You'll need to get the figures down in black and white if you want an accurate money picture. A list of questions something like this will help you know how much money is "enough."

— How much income is certain?
— What will essential expenses be?
   — housing

— food
— clothing
— tithes and offerings
— incidentals
— other items you consider essential
— What margin is there for emergencies?
— What shall we do about insurance and savings?
After some adding and subtracting you will be better able to make intelligent decisions. It's important for both to feel in all sincerity that they can be satisfied to live on such a budget day in and week out. Being willing to plan realistically before marriage for your financial needs is a good indication you'll be able to make your budget work after marriage.

Remember, the money you have is God's, for "The earth is the Lord's and the fullness thereof; the world, and they that dwell therein." (Psalm 24:1). Thankfully accept what He allows to come into your hands, and prayerfully ask His guidance in using it.

Any financial planning must recognize the fact that in marriage, your money needs will increase. When you're married you will want to add "this table" or "that picture" to make your home more attractive. You'll want to entertain your friends and relatives, at least occasionally. Being married means you'll probably want a baby before too long. All of these joys of marriage demand money. You'll discover that, far from the proverb of "two being able to live as cheaply as one," marriage may sometimes prove that two together cannot live as cheaply as two apart!

"Happily Ever After"

The fairy love stories of childhood took any prince and princess . . . waved the magic wand of love . . . and they lived happily ever after!

Your love story will be somewhat different. There will be no prince, no princess, no magic wand. But you can be quite sure of the "Happily ever after" ending if you are willing to approach marriage with thoughtful preparation.

Such preparation means
— knowing what makes a happy marriage
  — being ready for marriage
    — loving a person who is right for you
      — having adequate financial security
        — knowing the family of the one you are to marry
          — and above all it means following God's guidance.

The couple who comes to marriage with these understandings has a firm foundation on which to build a happy life!

Questions and Answers

What is meant by "differences in love"?
There are many reasons why people "fall in love." Some are desirable reasons. Others, such as wanting to escape from parents, desiring someone to dominate, wanting to be "mothered," or wishing a convenient sex outlet are undesirable. Successful marriages are built upon love that stems from wholesome, desirable motives. Thoughtful young people will carefully examine the motives which underlie their love.

What about love making during engagement?
Wise couples do not become engaged to marry unless there are reasonable prospects of meeting the demands of establishing a home. During the engagement period couples will want to spend much time together, sharing future plans and displaying that respect and affection which is becoming to a wholesome Christian.

What is the place of spiritual maturity in marriage?
Just as it is normal for a child to grow, so is it normal for the new Christian to develop in the things of God. Spiritual growth is the result of prayer, study of God's Word, association with believers, witnessing and other types of Christian activities.

Because of the demands placed upon successful family living, spiritual maturity is required in both marriage partners. Young people should not enter into marriage unless they have-grown enough spiritually to have real spiritual discernment.

How can a couple that is contemplating marriage be assured that they will be able to make the necessary sex adjustments when they are married?

Physiological adjustments in marriage rarely present a problem unless serious, abnormal factors are involved. Much more serious are problems concerned with attitudes regarding sex. Actually, there is no such thing as a perfect adjustment because people themselves are imperfect.

Married couples who have a basic understanding of human anatomy, and whose lives are marked by respect, consideration and the Christian graces, seldom experience difficulty in sex adjustments. However, if such problems do present themselves, it is wise to seek professional help.

Is it advisable to marry one from a different race or culture?

Differences in cultures and races may present serious hindrances to successful marriage. This can be explained in the fact that such differences usually mean differences in opinion, differences in desires, differences in tastes, differences in beliefs, and differences in habits.

Naturally, marriage partners must cooperate if they are to be happy. But it is impossible for them to cooperate if they disagree in their opinions, desires, tastes, beliefs and habits.

A couple from different cultures may "fall in love" and overlook their differences long enough to get married, but as time goes on, it becomes apparent that basically, their differences in backgrounds are so marked that they have a most unhappy situation.

When those from different races marry, an additional burden of unacceptance is placed upon both the married partners and eventually upon their children.

Does the Bible teach that the husband is to be the head of the home?

Marriage is a partnership in which the husband and wife become "one flesh." They form a union, and as such they mutually, under God, guide the affairs of their family. God has ordained that the wife bear children and care for the home.

Upon the husband is placed the responsibility of providing for and protecting the family. Along with the responsibility of leadership in the home, the husband is charged with loving his wife, "even as Christ also loved the church, and gave himself for it."

A study of the Scriptures reveals a beautiful and matchless plan for successful family life (Ephesians 5, I Peter 3).

Occasionally, just before marriage, a Christian couple suddenly becomes frightened about going through with their wedding plans. Is this a sign that God does not approve of the marriage?

No, it's usually an emotional reaction. It's perfectly normal. Getting married is a big step. It's a life-time contract. Actually, the implications are enough to "scare" anyone!

5

How Our Bodies Grow

The Community Hospital was completely different on Friday morning. In fact it was then the most important place in the world to Dave Johnson. For months he and his wife had looked forward to the arrival of their little one, and now the day was here!

While doctors were preparing Marilyn for the delivery of the baby, Dave was talking excitedly to the lady at the business office on the first floor. Suddenly a voice from the loud speaker announced, "Mr. Johnson, calling Mr. David Johnson. Will you please come to the maternity ward on the third floor?"

Unaware of anything else, Dave rushed to the elevator. Although he forgot to call his floor, the operator knew only too well which floor needed him. As he stepped off, a nurse said happily, "Mr. Johnson, you have a baby girl!"

"Oh, uh, wonderful!" said Dave. And then he continued, "Uh, uh, how much does she weigh?"

Then, as if it were the first baby ever announced, she said, "Five pounds and thirteen ounces."

"Five pounds and thirteen ounces?" repeated **Dave.** "Well, uh, isn't that a little small?"

With a twinkle in her eyes and a voice of real assurance the nurse replied, "Maybe just a little small but she is all *there* and she will *grow!*"

And Connie *did* grow! In fact when the Johnsons took her to the doctor's office for her first check-up at the end of four weeks, she weighed in at eight pounds and four ounces — a nice average for a "one-monther"!

The fact that new-born babies are not all the same size gives us an important key to the understanding of all human growth, for each individual grows at his own particular rate. Some grow slowly, some rapidly. Some grow broad, some grow tall. But no matter how rapidly or how slowly an individual grows, all growth follows an orderly sequence of development from conception to maturity. How good to know that God has a well-organized plan for the way we'll grow!

Growth Begins

Life begins at that dramatic moment when the microscopic sperm from the father enters the ovum in the mother's body. From this two-cell beginning, cells divide and divide again; minute after minute, hour after hour, until in nine months the baby has grown large enough and strong enough to be born into the outside world.

A study of human growth reveals a thrilling story of God's handiwork. In many ways it is a mystery story! For who can explain exactly how the new baby can

develop from a living speck smaller than the tiniest seed?
Or who can look at the tiny newborn one and know
precisely what will take place to make this baby into
an adult?

At birth the baby is appealingly helpless and completely dependent upon those around him. He is usually
quite red, but wonderfully complete from his wispy hair
(which may or may not be abundant) to his tiny toe-
nails. The new baby's reactions are unstable; he startles,
cries, sneezes, or quivers on the slightest provocation.

THE FIRST YEAR

By the time four weeks have passed, however, the
baby is a much more steady little person. He reacts
happily to the comforts of being warm and well fed. He
responds to pain, discomfort and hunger with a persistent
and unhappy cry.

At four months the so-recently-born infant is a
smiling, responsive baby. He enjoys his world with eyes
which have become nimble and expressive.

But looking and seeing no longer satisfy the same
baby at seven months! Now he wants to touch and feel
all he can reach. He may sit well alone; if not, he likes
to sit on a lap or in a high chair.

By ten months the baby's motor skills are developing
rapidly. Some babies now creep, some stand alone, occasionally a baby even walks. But whatever his muscular
accomplishments, the baby has become an inquisitive little
individual who wants to poke and pry into everything
around him.

By the first birthday the baby is an extremely sociable little fellow. He laughs and jabbers and imitates. His vocabulary development has begun with "ma-ma" or "da-da" or other easily said words. But he usually shows little ability to talk until he is about two. At the end of his first year he may be walking or just getting ready for that first step.

In this first year the baby has grown in body as well as in other abilities. He has just about tripled his birth weight and probably has added about ten inches to his height. Although he will never again grow as rapidly as he has during his first year, all of the first three years are considered a rapid-growth period.

From One to Three

Add another year to the year-old, and his baby days are almost past. He is now able to use the toilet with a bit of help. He calls the members of his family by name. He likes his toys and is possessive with them. He can look at a book, turning the pages one at a time.

At the three year mark the child is able to do many things. He has learned to feed himself satisfactorily. He can help dress and undress himself. Socially he is finding enjoyment as he plays with other children, and he enjoys pleasing adults.

These observations of the way a child grows are based, of course, on average development. Naturally, there are always variations because of individual differences.

Most children are actually a little behind or a little ahead of the average. But this is immaterial. They are growing every day and each one will reach maturity according to his own growth timetable.

CHARACTERISTICS OF GROWTH

Surprisingly all parts of the body do not grow at the same time or rate. For example, the head grows most rapidly before birth. At birth it is one-fourth as long as the entire body; at maturity only one-eighth as long.

Arms and legs are short during childhood. Then at the adolescent period they lengthen very rapidly. Sometimes coordination has a hard time keeping up with growth!

The trunk — the part of the body between the neck and the legs — does not grow to adult size until the arms and legs have their length. In the early teens this short trunk gives many adolescents a short-waisted appearance.

FROM THREE TO TEN

From three to ten are years of slow and steady growth. Most boys and girls gain about two inches in height, more or less, each year. Many factors determine just how much a certain child will grow in a given year. Food, exercise, home conditions, size of parents, or health, may slow down or speed up the child's development.

Then when a girl is about ten or a little past, her growth seems to come to a standstill. Worried parents urge more rest, more food, more vitamins. But worry is not necessary, for strange as it may seem, growing does almost stop for six months to a year before the startling rapid growth of early adolescence.

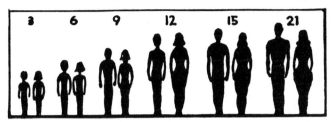

All boys and girls pass through similar developmental sequences, but they do not do so at the same age. Note the growth changes in height and shape of body in this chart. At the beginning of adolescence there is usually rapid growth.

Then Puberty

Suddenly, somewhere between her tenth and eleventh birthday or a bit later, everything is different. The girl usually begins to grow taller and at the same time heavier. Her legs and arms grow longer, her hands and feet larger. Her straight childish lines soften into rounded curves. This growth-spurt of puberty, which lasts about two years, often takes the girl from childhood to the threshold of womanhood.

But where are the boys? During the ten to eleven-year-old time they are left behind! Fortunately, they are too busy building models or playing baseball to brood over being shorter than most girls of the same age. Then, sometime around twelve, most boys come to their period of little growth, which may last for six months or a year. Just as with the girls, this is followed by a period of rapid growing. The boy grows tall. He also grows heavier. Then his heart and lungs and muscles strengthen to care for the nearly man-sized body. The face changes from the little boy lines to become more mature. This growth spurt usually lasts from two to three years so that at fifteen, or a bit older, most boys are as tall or taller than the girls their own age! Boyhood has been left behind and the fellow is now a young man.

DUCT GLANDS

During this time of rapid growth the duct glands in the skin, which are the oil and sweat glands, become very active in both boys and girls. For this reason the smart teenager uses much soap and water. Nothing is more effective than plenty of warm water and soap to keep the accumulation of oil at a minimum. This is helpful in controlling the blemishes which often appear on the face during this maturing time. Both boys and girls need to remember that soap and water are not always enough to prevent perspiration odors. A deodorant faithfully used will make certain the teenager does not offend others. This increase of perspiration and oil secretion is just another part of growing up!

DUCTLESS GLANDS

The period of puberty does not just happen. Rather, it is the result of interesting and dramatic changes which take place deep within the body of the girl or boy.

These changes are largely governed by the ductless glands which are tiny organs in the body. Tiny, but important, for these glands secrete substances called hormones which are vital to proper development.

The pituitary gland, located in the head, is one of the most important of these ductless glands. Tallness, shortness, sexual development, and other phases of growth are controlled by this gland. It acts much like a policeman giving the go-ahead signals for growth. For the hormones of the pituitary gland stimulate other ductless glands into activity at puberty.

From birth each girl has deep in her lower abdomen two almond-shaped ovaries. These are ductless glands which are inactive during childhood. At puberty hormones from the pituitary gland stimulate the ovaries into activity. This is vitally important to the girl, for the now active ovaries produce other hormones which take the girl into womanhood and cause her to retain her femininity throughout her life.

The boy's growth toward manhood and his masculinity throughout life, are controlled by hormones from the testes, two glands which are below the trunk of the boy's body. These glands also depend on the secretions of the pituitary gland to stimulate them into activity. And so at puberty the testes, which have been inactive during childhood begin to perform their duty — to change a boy into a man.

These interesting facts about growth show us that a child does not grow steadily each day between babyhood and maturity. Instead, he grows by a series of starts and stops. Sometimes his growth is extremely fast. Occasionally he stops growing for a time, apparently to gather strength for his next spurt of development. No two children grow exactly alike, but in spite of the individual differences God's plan of growth finally brings each person to maturity.

HUMAN GROWTH — A DIVINE PLAN

The Scriptures declare, "The works of the Lord are great." Certainly the miracle of human growth and development is one of God's supreme works. Matchless in genius is the plan for the growth of man! God controls the development of each organ of the body in masterful fashion. If, after birth, the human body should continue to grow at the same rate that it grows before birth, each of us would be many times larger than the moon by the time we reached the age of twenty-one! But our great Creator, in His matchless wisdom, regulates the human body so that it develops appropriately, and in orderly sequence.

When we think of the limitless universe, of which the Psalmist wrote when he said, "When I consider Thy heavens, the work of Thy fingers, the moon and the stars which Thou hast ordained," we may tend to forget the greatness of the human body. David also said that "we are fearfully and wonderfully made." The same God who planned and established the wonders of the telescopic universe, has so intricately designed our bodies, even to our most microscopic atom, that we should, in the humility of great awe, exclaim, "What is man that Thou art mindful of him?" Surely our voice of praise should ever be, "Oh Lord, our Lord, how excellent is Thy name *in all the earth!*"

Questions and Answers

How heavy and how long is a newborn baby?
The size of newborn babies varies greatly at birth, boys being slightly heavier and longer than girls. Most newborns are from eighteen to twenty-two inches long and between six and nine pounds in weight. However, a baby may be somewhat shorter or longer, lighter or heavier, and be perfectly normal.

Why do new born babies have trouble seeing?
Babies can and do see, but they have not yet grown accustomed to the bright world outside of their mother's body. It also takes time for them to develop the ability to focus their eyes and to distinguish colors. They can tell light from darkness but they cannot see far. These abilities, however, will all gradually develop.

Could something happen to cause a baby to stay small all his life?
Very seldom does this happen. In rare cases the pituitary gland has failed to function properly and the person remains a dwarf. On the other hand if the pituitary gland is over active one could be a giant. However, such cases are extremely rare.

Do all parts of the body grow at the same time?

No, all parts of the body do not grow at the same time. The head grows most rapidly before birth. The brain and the muscles have their greatest growth period during childhood. The early adolescent period is the time of rapid growth for the arms and legs, while the trunk does not reach full growth until maturity.

When does a child grow most rapidly?

Each individual has two periods of rapid growth. The first period comes in the months immediately following birth. The second rapid growth period comes with adolescence and continues until maturity.

Why, in Junior High, do some boys and girls still look like children, while others look like young men and women?

No two children grow at the same speed. This difference in size is normal. The tall children have already reached the adolescent period of rapid growth. It will come to the shorter ones in time.

If a boy of thirteen starts to grow faster than another boy, does it mean he is going to be taller when he is grown?

Not necessarily. God does not use the same pattern. There are many individual differences. The shorter boy may soon overtake the taller one.

What controls our growth?

Tiny organs within our bodies called glands, control our growth. The pituitary gland, which is located in the head, is one of the most important. Other glands working with the pituitary regulate our sexual development. These are the testes in the boy and the ovaries in a girl.

What makes one person tall and another short?
The size of the parents greatly influences an individual's adult size. Many factors determine just how much a certain child will grow during a given year. Food, exercise, home conditions, or general health all play a part. But the size of an adult is determined to a great extent by heredity.

Why do some teenagers have pimples on their faces?
During adolescence the oil glands, which are in the skin, become very active. These glands produce a great deal of oil which sometimes collects in small pimples. These pimples may become swollen and infected. Teenage people should use much soap and water to help eliminate excess oil. Plenty of sleep, sunshine and a well-balanced diet will also help control this skin difficulty. In extreme cases a doctor's prescription may be necessary.

Why does a woman develop such a different figure from a man?
The bodies of men and women were intended by God for different purposes. God said man would earn his food by toil so He gave to man a stronger body with broader shoulders and larger muscles. The woman, God said, would give birth to children so He has given her an appropriate body. Her hips become broader and her abdomen longer than the man's so that her body may accommodate itself to the growth and birth of children. Of course the baby is also provided for by the woman's breasts which supply the baby with milk.

6

God's Masterpiece

Perhaps even more awe-inspiring than the process of physical growth is the wonder of God's design in bringing to maturity the sexual organs; and the subsequent mating process and fertilization. Every believer should thrill to the realization that he is spiritually related in a personal way to the God of all creation. In this chapter we shall draw aside the curtain in order to view this next wonderful exhibition of God's creative power, seen in the consummation of the sex development.

BODY CHANGES — A FUNCTION OF THE SEX GLANDS

In some respects life really begins, not at forty, but near fourteen! As stated previously, there is a physical revolution during the early years of the teens. That period of sudden physical growth is accompanied by noticeable changes produced by the sex glands. This period, called puberty, is the time when the sex glands surge to activity by secreting their hormones.

As noted previously, the pituitary gland and the sex glands are related. At least they "converse" with each other. Before the sex glands can become active in adolescence, the pituitary gland first sends a message to them. After hormones have begun to be produced by the boy's testes and the girl's ovaries, the pituitary gland slows up its production of hormones. The wonderful unity and cooperation between these two glands is amazing!

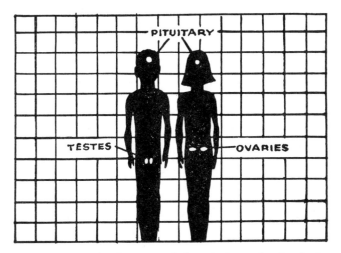

Note the location of the pituitary glands of the head, and the testes and ovaries of the pubic region. These tiny, but important organs control the growth of the body.

This new contribution of the sex glands brings about many important changes. Courtesy suggests that we consider the young lady before the young man, noting the effects upon her appearance.

SEXUAL DEVELOPMENT OF THE GIRL

As a result of the hormones sent forth by the ovaries, the girl approaching puberty will find hair appearing under the arms and in the pubic region. In addition, hair will become thicker on the arms and legs. Sometimes girls, especially those with dark hair, will find that the fine down on the sides of their face and on the upper lip becomes more noticeable.

The function of the female sex hormone is to cause the girl's voice to deepen a little, hair to grow on the body, and the breasts to develop, changes which occur in the process of maturation.

The girl's voice also undergoes a change, though not as radical as the boy's. It gradually becomes deeper, as well as richer and fuller.

In this period of maturing the girl's breasts develop. Located in the breasts are glands called mammary or milk-producing glands. These become larger, thus preparing girls for the demands of motherhood. During this period of growth the breasts may feel tender or sensitive for a time. Girls may recognize that these changes are God's way of preparing them for that cherished time in marriage when they will care for their own tiny baby. Of course some girls do not develop at the same rate of speed or to the same proportions as other girls. These differences are quite normal, varying with the individual.

Other noticeable areas of change for the girl are the sexual organs and the hips. The sex organs become larger, and the hips become more rounded, assuming a more feminine appearance. These are days of definite maturing for the young lady. The time spent in combing her hair, experimenting with that new perfume, using new and dainty undergarments, are all a part of reaching adulthood.

SEXUAL DEVELOPMENT OF THE BOY

In the boy, changes accompany the secretions of the hormones by the testes. A sudden spurt of growth usually occurs later than it does in girls. During this time the male sex organs increase in size. Whiskers begin sprouting, and fellows begin looking into mirrors, in search of excuses for shaving! Hair begins to appear on the body, — on the legs, under and on the arms, in the pubic region, and perhaps on the chest. In fact, the word *puberty* comes from the Latin verb *pubescere*, which means "to become hairy." Every Christian fellow should realize that this sudden surge of manliness is all in God's design.

A significant contribution to a fellow's pride during these days is his incipient beard. This in itself is an interesting phenomenon. The soft hairs above the upper lip first become darker and thus more obvious. Then the hair on the cheeks darkens giving the appearance of "sideburns" down the side of the face. Finally the hair on the throat becomes rather coarse and long. By this time, of course, the young man has begun to shave.

The male sex hormone brings about the appearance of whiskers, the growth of body hair, and the deepening of the voice.

The voice also is affected by these active sex hormones. As a child his voice was high, but at adolescence it begins to deepen. It is during this period that embarrassing moments come because the voice plays those unpredictable tricks such as "cracking" in the middle of a sentence. The explanation for this is to be found in the increasing size of the voice box and in the lengthening of the vocal cords. Soon, however, the full masculine tones are to be heard whether they be tenor or bass.

It is during this age of puberty that the body assumes masculine shape too. The boy becomes more muscular with broad shoulders and narrow hips. By high school graduation time or before, he does handsome justice to a man's suits!

ANOTHER FUNCTION OF THE SEX GLANDS — PRODUCTION OF SEX CELLS

Besides producing the body changes just mentioned, God accomplishes a second purpose through the sex glands. As boys and girls become sexually mature these glands produce male and female sex cells. These tiny cells are the instruments in God's hand for human reproduction. Their union inside the female is the beginning of a new life and is therefore very important.

The male cell is known as the sperm cell or spermatozoan and is first produced in its mature condition at puberty. This tiny sperm cell is surprisingly small, only one five-hundredth of an inch in size. For this reason it cannot be seen without the aid of a microscope. We know, however, that when magnified many times it looks much like a tadpole. It has a head, containing a tiny round spot called the nucleus, and a long thread-like tail which propels it at considerable speed.

Much larger than the sperm cell is the female cell called the ovum or egg cell. Although it is the largest known single cell in the human body, it is nevertheless smaller than a pinpoint. The nucleus of the ovum is surrounded by the outer edge or cell wall, which is called the nuclear membrane.

With this introduction to the cells themselves let us turn to a study of the sex organs which produce them.

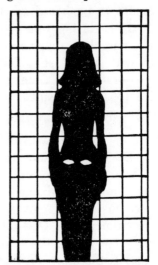

Ova (female egg cells) are produced by the ovaries. Each ovum, no longer than a pin point, has a round nucleus inside (see illustration).

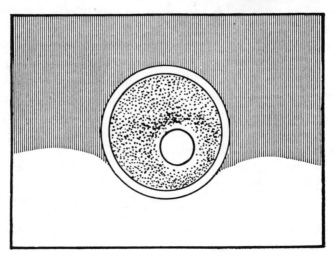

THE GIRL'S SEX ORGANS

The girl's sex organs are for the most part inside the body. In addition to the sex glands, or ovaries, the important parts include the vulva, the vagina, the uterus and the Fallopian tubes.

The outside portion of the girl's sex organs, located where the trunk joins the legs, is called the vulva. It is composed of thick folds of skin with tissues underneath and a groove running between these folds which are known as outer lips. Just inside these outer lips are thinner folds of tissue called inner lips. These folds serve a distinct purpose, which is to protect the two openings in this region. At the top of the vulva is an opening which is used to discharge urine (waste fluid of the kidneys). A little farther back is the opening called the vagina. Partly covering the opening to the vagina there is usually a fold of membrane called the hymen. This membrane may or may not be present in unmarried girls.

The vagina is a canal about four inches long which extends backward and upward inside the body. A stretchy muscle fiber with rough texture composes its walls.

The upper end of the vagina joins the uterus, a hollow, pear-shaped organ with elastic muscular walls. It is the uterus which provides the conditions favorable for the union of the sperm and ovum and so becomes the early home for the baby. Being elastic, the uterus can stretch to many times its size to allow for the growing baby.

Opening into the upper part of the uterus are two tubes, one on each side. Each tube extends away from the uterus for three inches or so and curves partially around an ovary. These tubes are delicate passages for the ova from the ovaries to the uterus, and are lined with cilia, fine moving hair-like processes. The cilia force the ova toward the uterus.

Located on the right and left of the uterus are the two ovaries, the sex organs which produce hormones and sex cells. The ovaries are thin and oval shaped, one to two inches long, about an inch wide and one-fourth of an inch thick. They resemble an almond in size and shape. Contained within one small round chamber are many immature egg cells. One of these cells is called an ovum. More than one are called ova. When a girl reaches puberty one of these tiny chambers opens and releases a mature, or ripe, ovum. This process is called ovulation, and usually occurs only once every twenty-eight days. This is a remarkable display of God's magnificent design, since there are thousands of cells within each ovary, yet, taking turns, the ovaries release only one mature cell every month.

The ovum now begins a trip to the uterus, which is an interesting story in itself. After being released by the ovary it resides for a short time in the abdominal cavity in the vicinity of the open funnel-shaped tube. Soon however, it is caught by the finger-like tips of the tube and drawn into the tube. Again it finds help, for within the tube are hairs called cilia which, with the aid of the muscled walls of the tube itself, convey the tiny cell to the uterus. Should these hairs move in the wrong direction the ovum would never reach its appointed place and conception, the beginning of a new life, would not take place. But our sovereign God, who watches the sparrow's fall,

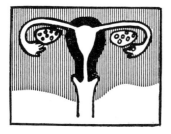

An ovum ripens and leaves the ovary about once a month from the period of adolescence on.

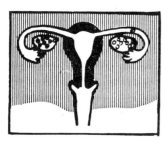

After the ovum leaves the ovary, it is drawn into the tube.

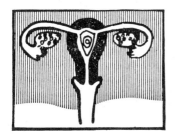

Over a period of days, as this ovum moves along the tube and into the uterus, an inner lining, richly supplied with blood, forms within the uterus.

knows the need of this minute cell and so makes appropriate provision.

Meanwhile, the uterus is preparing nourishment for the expected fertilized egg. Extra blood and tissue are supplied in case the ovum meets with a sperm cell of the male thereby creating a new speck of human life. If, however, the ovum fails to meet a sperm cell, the innermost layer of tissue, with accompanying blood is discharged, because the uterus no longer needs this lining. It leaves the body through the vagina, continuing its flow for a few days. This process is called menstruation, coming from the Latin word *mensis* meaning month, since the menstrual period takes place monthly.

It follows, of course, that ovulation also occurs monthly — about two weeks after menstruation. This process of ovulation begins, however, immediately after menstruation; that is, the uterus starts again to build up blood and tissue and another egg is released and starts its journey to the uterus. Month after month this process occurs, being interrupted only by fertilization, when an egg is joined by a sperm and attaches itself to the uterus, thus commencing a pregnancy.

Girls undergo a new and eventful experience when this process of menstruation begins at puberty. It is God's established method of regulating the health and fertility of the sex organs. Naturally, an understanding of the purpose and role of ovulation and menstruation is helpful in developing a happy, positive attitude toward this new process. It means that a girl is approaching womanhood — graduating from a little girl into a grown-up!

Some girls have their first menstrual period as early at ten or eleven years of age. Others may experience it as late as sixteen or seventeen. It is likely that the first menstrual periods will be irregular, some beginning a few days early or a few days late. In some cases it may even skip a month. Within a year or two, however, regularity is usually established.

The length of periods and time between periods called cycles also vary from woman to woman. The flow may take anywhere from two to seven days, but it usually begins heavily and then decreases until it stops. Some cycles are as short as twenty-one days; others as long as thirty-five days, but generally, they are about twenty-eight days. Each girl will become acquainted with her own particular pattern. Since illness, emotional upsets and other conditions may alter the number of days between menstrual periods, one need not be unduly concerned about occasional irregularities.

Activities for the girls during the menstrual period need not be curtailed. Some physical exercise is often beneficial on the first day or two as an aid in the functioning of the body. However, girls should avoid too strenuous exercise. Most girls are more sensitive to extremes in temperatures during this time and for this reason excessive heat or cold should be avoided. This is not to say that a warm bath is out of order. To the contrary, such becomes even more needful, for along with the sanitary napkins this helps to keep the body in a clean condition.

While most women and girls feel reasonably well during their time of menstruation, some will feel irritable and uncomfortable, and a few will have rather severe pains in the lower abdomen and back. If one has prolonged severe cramps, she should consult a doctor. Generally speaking, however, a girl should not pamper herself and life should continue much as usual. But others of the family should be particularly understanding when she is experiencing her monthly "period."

This monthly cycle usually continues through the years until a woman reaches her middle forties. At such time menstruation will become increasingly irregular, and then finally stops. This time is known as the menopause or "change of life." It marks the time when fertilization is no longer possible, because the ovaries cease to produce mature egg cells and the sex hormones are produced in much smaller amounts. The time of menopause will vary with each woman, though for most, the change will take place over a period of several years. Although some women at this time do not always feel well, life in general should go on as usual.

THE BOY'S SEX ORGANS

As previously stated, the female sex organs are largely internal. Just the opposite is true for the male. Although the two main tubes are inside the body, the penis and testes extend outside the body. The testes, or testicles, are contained in the scrotum, a pouch of loose skin which hangs just behind the penis. God's care and design are evidenced again by this fact, for the stored up sperm cells cannot withstand the higher temperatures present within the body. For this cause God has provided appropriate muscles which relax and thus allow the testes to hang lower in warm weather, and which draw the testes slightly closer to the body in cooler weather.

Normally both testes descend to their proper place inside the scrotum at birth. However, occasionally one

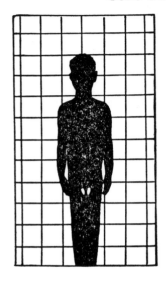

The male sex cells, called sperm, are produced by the testes. Each sperm, so small that it can be seen only with a microscope, has a head, containing the nucleus and a long thread-like tail that wiggles and causes movement of the cell.

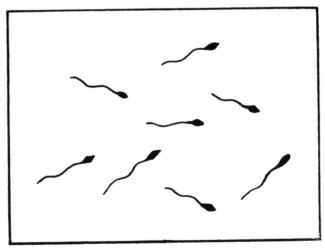

testis may fail to descend and so remains inside the body. If this condition occurs, it should and usually can be corrected by a medical doctor. If both testes are allowed to remain within the body, conditions are such as to hinder the normal production of sperm cells and therefore the boy is sterile, unable to become a father. The testes are egg-shaped, approximately an inch thick and one and three-fourths inches long. Usually one descends slightly more than the other. Like the ovary the testis contains many tiny chambers or sections separated by partitions. There are about two or three hundred of these chambers in each testis and each chamber is filled with thread-like tightly coiled tubes. Sperm cells are produced within these narrow tubes or tubules, which number several hundred in each testis.

Storage space for the cells which are produced is immediately behind each testis, meaning of course that this space is also within the scrotum. Millions of cells are stored here at a time. During mating, when the nervous system gives the signal, the sperm passes out through the tubes and out of the penis.

This tube through which the sperm passes is called the main sperm duct. It joins the storage place in the scrotum on one end and then passes into the lower abdomen, circling then around the bladder. Each testis has its own duct, both of which finally enter a single channel which then leads out through the penis.

Although this channel is used as a passage-way for both urine and sperm-carrying fluid, the two never leave the body at the same time. There are certain nerves which act as sentinels permitting exit to only one at a time. The tube bringing urine is shut off whenever the sperm cells are to pass through.

Along the path of these two main ducts from the two testes are several glands, some of which produce a thick, whitish fluid called semen in which the sperm cells swim.

Like the vulva of the female, the penis of the male is located in front of the body at the lower region of the abdomen. Like other parts of the body it may vary slightly from person to person. Because of religious or sanitary reasons, parents usually have baby boys circumcised. This is a minor operation which entails removal of the cap or foreskin covering the sensitive tip of the penis. Bible students will recall that this had special significance for the children of Israel, as the outward sign of God's covenant made with Abraham. (See Genesis 17:1-11.)

Usually the penis hangs down, limp. However, during times of sexual excitement blood rushes to the penis causing the spongy tissues to swell, making the penis enlarged and rigid. This condition is called an erection and must exist before sperm cells can leave the body. However, sperm cells do not leave the body every time the penis is erect — usually just during mating or when manipulated, or sometimes during sleep.

This release of sperm cells during sleep may puzzle boys who first experience it during adolescence. However, it should not cause concern. It is a natural, normal function which releases a small quantity of fluid, leaving a sticky substance on the sheets or pajamas. It indicates that sexual maturity has been reached. This release is called a seminal emission, or more commonly "wet dream," because a dream usually accompanies the event. Unlike urinating, it happens automatically and without warning.

It is equally natural for boys and men to awake in the morning with the penis erect. This may be caused by the bladder being filled with urine, consequently pressing on certain glands.

Some men in later life pass through a period which is comparable to menopause for women. It is a time of decreasing production of sex hormones. When this time is reached, men are less likely to become fathers than they were in earlier years.

The two functions of the sex glands then, are the producing of body changes and of cells. A further consideration will be the union of cells and consequent fertilization of the egg cell.

MATING

Marriage is of God. In the beginning He made them male and female (Genesis 1:27). His purpose was at least two-fold. It became apparent that it was not good for man to be alone. Adam was a social being, so God created "an help meet" to share his joys and tasks, his life in the garden and his fellowship with God. The second reason is that this was God's ordained way for populating the earth (Genesis 1:28). As Adam and Eve in innocence expressed their deepest affection for one another, God purposed that this should be the means of bringing forth children. "The two become one flesh" (Genesis 2:24).

Therefore it is God's provision that man and woman should be united in desires, purposes, feelings, life as a whole. Part of this union is physical. The highest expression of physical love is the mating act, by which husband and wife can produce children.

'Biblically speaking, mating is the "making of the two one flesh." Physiologically, mating is the entering of the penis into the vagina of the wife. The God-intended physical attraction of the wife's body for the husband's, and of the husband's body for the wife's, combined with the love which they share, causes an increased supply of blood to flow into the sex organs. This causes an erection in the husband.

These preparations for the sexual union are accompanied by caresses and other expressions of love. As the husband and wife embrace, emotion mounts, and at the same time the vagina releases secretions which serve to lubricate it, as the erect penis fits into its opening. As husband and wife express their love in this way, excitement increases until a climax is reached at which time semen passes from the penis into the upper part of the vagina. Immediately after the climax there is a subsiding of excitement, replaced by a sense of contentment.

The semen which has been released is not of great quantity but it contains millions of tiny sperm cells. The tails of these sperm cells move back and forth propelling the cell through the vagina up to the uterus and from there into the narrow tubes. The time required for this trip is from one to several hours.

If it happens to be the time of the month when the egg cell is making its way through the tube to the

uterus, the two cells will unite and fertilization will be
likely to take place. It will be a month before the wife
will be able to tell whether or not this is so. The first indication will probably be the omission of a menstrual period.
Should this occur she should consult her doctor to see if
a new life has actually begun. During the early months
of pregnancy, the wife may experience some nausea or
sickness, but this will usually not continue long.

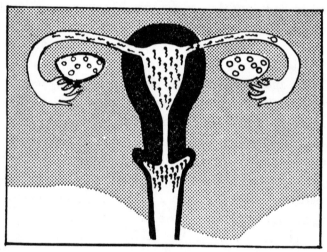

The sperm cells, propelled by their thread-like
tails, move into the uterus and tubes.

FERTILIZATION

One of man's greatest joys and responsibilities is the
privilege of being a partner with God in this great creative
act. A new life has begun! What has actually taken place

is this: thousands of male sperm cells have gathered around the cell wall of the female ovum. As each tries to enter the egg, one, and only one, finally succeeds. The other sperm cells die since they cannot long remain alive in the mother's body. Many have not survived the trip from the vagina, through the uterus to the tubes.

And what happens to the one which enters the ovum? The tail drops off as the head containing the nucleus is plunged into the ripe egg. The nucleus then grows larger and unites with the nucleus of the egg.

As it starts to move slowly toward the uterus, the fertilized ovum begins to divide, making two cells. The two then divide making four, then eight, sixteen, and so on. It continues multiplying in geometric progression, thus becoming a ball of cells which ultimately develops into a baby with more than two-hundred billion cells!

CELLS

At this point an examination of the actual structure of cells is especially important, since it helps us to understand the difference between babies. As previously indicated, each cell contains a nucleus. This disc-like spot in the center is surrounded by a substance which contains the material for nourishing the cell; the protective wall on the outside encloses this substance.

Within the nucleus are other tiny structures which we call chromosomes. A study of these minute bodies should again cause us to say with the Psalmist, "I will praise Thee; for I am fearfully and wonderfully made" (Psalm 139:14). They are so small that only a very high-powered microscope will adequately reveal them, yet God has chosen to use these tiny bodies for the transference of family resemblances and hereditary traits.

God's handiwork is further noticed in the mathematically accurate arrangement of these chromosomes. Most of the cells in the body — nerve cells, bone cells, blood cells, muscle cells, have forty-eight chromosomes each. However, planning was not omitted in the sex cell, for they — the sperm and the ovum — each contain twenty-four chromosomes. Therefore when they unite in fertilization the ovum has forty-eight chromosomes just like the other cells. Half of these will be from the father and half from the mother. When the fertilized egg divides, the chromosomes also divide, leaving the proper number of cells in the new life.

Not all chromosomes are alike. Some are straight, some bent, some thread-like. Within each of them, however, are thousands upon thousands of microscopic parts, called genes. Arranged in bead-like fashion, these genes are the particular means of producing the individual physical differences between people, such as color of eyes and hair, the size of the body, etc. Besides this function they also determine what parts of the body cells will ultimately become, since these cells become skin, hair, muscles, and other parts of the body.

The genes are the causes for one's resemblance to his parents. Traits passed on in this fashion are said to be inherited.

An additional body of knowledge concerns the birth

of twins. It has already been pointed out that each month an ovary releases one ovum which makes its way to the uterus through the tube. Occasionally, however, both ovaries send forth an ovum at the same time or perhaps one ovary will send out two ova. In case these two ova meet sperm cells and fertilization takes place, twins are the result.

Two such separately fertilized eggs form what are commonly called unlike, or fraternal twins. These usually look no more alike than other brothers and sisters, even though they are born on the same day. During the development of these twins each is joined to the mother at a different place in the uterus and each has his own separate sac in which to grow.

The birth of identical twins is the result of the division of one egg at the time of the first separation. Such twins grow in the same sac in the uterus and are attached by their cords to the same spot. Identical twins are always of the same sex and are very difficult to distinguish from each other.

Triplets and quadruplets may be formed either by the division of one cell or a fertilization of three or four cells, or even by a combination of the two ways. Any birth of two or more babies is known as a multiple birth.

Although man can understand the basic theory of human reproduction, the actual creation of the body — sight, the other senses, the brain, and other parts of the body — is truly beyond human comprehension.

Any rational man must come to the conclusion that

only God could produce such an intelligent creature which alone has a capacity for God-consciousness. A study of the human body causes every believer to stand in awe and reverence, compelling him to trust implicitly in the One who created him and who died to redeem him!

Questions and Answers

Do the sex glands do anything besides produce reproductive cells?

Yes, The hormones they secrete play a big part in the development of masculine and feminine physical traits during adolescence.

Why do women menstruate?

Once a woman's ovaries begin to produce egg cells each month, changes take place in the uterus every time the ovaries release egg cells. The uterus prepares itself by building up extra blood and tissue for the nourishment of a fertilized egg, if such should reach it. If no fertile egg reaches it, the uterus will slough off some of this blood and tissue and will return to normal. The onset of menstruation means that a young girl is growing up into womanhood and that the potential of childbearing is present.

What causes cramps in girls?

There are several causes. Nervousness or an upset condition could be responsible. It may be that the uterus is out of position in the woman's abdomen, or that certain hormones which help in menstruation are being produced in insufficient quantity. However, cramps are not significant unless they persist, and then a girl is wise to consult her doctor.

What does it mean if a girl's period is late or perhaps skipped entirely?

It is not uncommon for the flow to be two or three days early or late, especially with young girls who are just beginning to menstruate. Their flow may be quite irregular. A skipped period may indicate pregnancy, but not necessarily so. Frequent delays and irregularities warrant a doctor's counsel.

When do women stop menstruating?

Most women enter menopause or "change of life" gradually in the mid-forties, and then menstruation begins to dwindle. This means that the ovaries become inactive in the production of egg cells, so the uterus need no longer prepare itself for babies since fertilization is no longer possible.

What is a seminal emission?

Sometimes during sleep, semen is discharged from the penis. It may be accompanied by a dream known as a "wet dream." This is a normal function of the body, usually occurring for the first time in adolescence.

How do sperm cells get in contact with egg cells?
During mating, millions of sperm cells are deposited in the vagina through the penis. In their liquid medium called semen, they begin to swim by wiggling their tails up the vagina, through the uterus and into the Fallopian tubes where they meet the egg cell.

What length of time is required for the penis to remain in the vagina in order to release sperm cells?
This varies. Sometimes only a few minutes are necessary. But the length of time depends upon the husband and wife who learn to fully meet their mutual desires.

How many sperm cells are required to fertilize an egg cell?
Of the many, tiny sperm cells that start the journey up the vagina, only a few reach their destination, and of these, only one penetrates the egg to complete fertilization.

What happens if sperm cells enter the vagina when the uterus already bears a fertilized egg?
Nothing happens. The pituitary gland controls the production of the ovaries, and when one egg has been fertilized, no more will be sent forth until after childbirth.

Will a wife always become pregnant after mating?
No. Only during a relatively short period during the month is fertilization possible. Even during this period, no sperm may be able to penetrate the egg cell. Furthermore, there is the possibility of sterility in either husband or wife.

Where is the baby's home in the mother during pregnancy?

The baby grows and develops in a hollow, pear-shaped organ called the uterus. The uterus is located in the lower part of the abdomen in front of the intestines and is connected with the outside of the woman's body by the vagina. The uterus is made of very elastic muscle tissue, so that it can expand to many times its normal size as the baby grows. In the Scripture, the uterus is referred to as the "womb."

What causes resemblance between parent and child?

The nucleus within the sex cell contains chemical units called chromosomes and genes which determine certain physical traits in the new baby. Since these units in the child are the sum of the same units in its parents, we might well expect that the child will bear some of the traits of its parents.

What is the explanation for twins?

One egg from each of the two tubes may become fertile as a result of mating. This is one way to account for twins. Another cause of twins is the division of the one egg in one of the tubes. The two halves separate and develop into two babies.

7

The Story of Birth

John Taylor was as comfortable as he could be! After reading the evening paper, he took off his shoes and stretched out on the soft divan. His wife, Gwen, had curled up in the rocker and was casually thumbing through a magazine.

"Honey," she said, "I've just been wondering about something."

"Wondering about what?" asked John.

"Well, uh," she continued, "about my period. I'm almost a week overdue now and it's never been like this — I'm always so regular."

"You've been feeling O.K., haven't you?" he asked.

"Oh, sure," she replied, "but I've been wondering if . . ."

". . . if maybe we're going to have a baby?" asked John, as he propped himself up with one arm and looked intently into her eyes.

Gwen put her magazine on the coffee table and sat down beside John. "Of course," she said, "no one can tell yet, but wouldn't it be wonderful if it were true?" Giving her a tight hug and looking into her happy face, he said, "Darling, I'll be the proudest husband in the world if it is true! How long will it be before we can tell for sure?"

"I don't know," she replied, "I suppose it will be several weeks before the doctor can give any reliable tests. But maybe we better not get our hopes too high. This may only be a false alarm."

But the Taylors didn't have their hopes too high, for a few weeks later an examination by the obstetrician revealed that Gwen was going to have a baby! Although they had never thought much about it before, John and Gwen had suddenly become very much interested in the development of the tiny life which God had entrusted to them.

Beyond all the other intricacies of human anatomy, nothing is as wonderful as the conception and growth of a baby within its mother. Little wonder that Jesus compared spiritual birth with physical birth (John 3:4-7). To give an adequate explanation of either, apart from the hand of God's omnipotence, is an impossibility. Does not the growth of a speck of living matter, smaller than the tiniest seed, into a mature human body witness to this fact? During the nine short months in which a fertilized ovum becomes a full sized baby, its living matter increases in weight to several billion times what it was originally. In order to get the full force of what actually takes place in this process, let us trace the history of a new life from the moment of its inception.

GROWTH-RECORD OF AN UNBORN BABY

During the process of mating, the sperm cells (spermatozoan) of the father pass from the penis into the vagina of the mother. The sperm cells then find their way through the uterus into the Fallopian tubes. If a sperm cell penetrates the ripe egg which has been discharged from the ovary, fertilization occurs. From this moment, a rapid multiplication of cells takes place within the embryo. The original fertilized egg cell divides into two cells, each new cell owning all of the same chromosomes and genes that were created when the sperm of the father and the ovum of the mother united. Then the two cells which first divided, again split into two, making four cells. The cells grow and divide, multiplying at a breath-taking rate during the early stages of life.

The sex of the baby is set from the time of fertilization, and nothing can change it. All of the egg cells which the ovaries of the mother produce are of one sort, but not so with the sperm cells of the father. There are two types of sperm cells, and if the egg is fertilized with a sperm cell having an X chromosome, the baby is a girl; if fertilized with a sperm cell having a Y chromosome, it is a boy. In a sense it is purely a matter of chance as to which of the two types of sperm cells will fertilize the egg. There is no way of predicting which of the two will (all fathers have both types) nor is there any certain method of telling, prior to birth, whether the embryo or fetus within the mother is a boy or a girl. This is God's secret for nine months. However, the lives of Christian couples are not left to "chance." Their heavenly Father is interested in every phase of their lives. So, through trusting in God and praying for His best, God will surely give them the child which in His divine plan is best — be it a boy or a girl.

The fertile egg travels through the tube to the uterus, and after about a week imbeds itself in the rich inner lining of the uterus, which has been built up in preparation for it.

After growing into a small mass of cells, the egg becomes longer and flattens out. Presently, three layers form within the living mass, and from these the various parts of the body will eventually emerge. These cells differentiate and become other systems. The outer layer of cells becomes the skin and the nervous system, including brain, spinal cord and nerves. The middle layer forms the blood vessels, blood, bones and muscles. The inner layer comes to be the digestive organs of the body, that is, the stomach, liver, kidneys and intestines. Could any mere man comprehend the amazing process by which this transformation takes place? At work here is the intricate designing power of God!

It is most interesting to note the development of the embryo during the nine months of pregnancy. After four weeks it is a very tiny being, about the size of a garden pea. Its weight is only a fraction of an ounce, although this is already an increase in size of fifty times. A few organs have begun to take shape, but it does not appear the least bit human.

By the second month the embryo is more clearly recognizable as human, though incredibly tiny to bear that resemblance. It is probably scarcely more than an inch in length. Numerous parts of the body are discernible by this time. Studies reveal that the heart and some other organs are functioning during the second month.

By the third month the embryo is called a fetus. Its development is much greater, yet it is still no more than three or four inches in length. Limbs, hands, fingers, toes and ears are taking shape. Its form is definitely human but its head is proportionately large for the rest of the body.

The fourth month brings more changes. Muscles are usable and limb movements may sometimes be felt by the mother. The heartbeat can be heard through a stethoscope. The skin is reddish and somewhat transparent, so that the blood vessels underneath are visible. The fetus is covered with very fine hair which will disappear during the eighth or ninth month. It has achieved nearly half its birth length, being about six to eight inches long, and weighs five or six ounces.

By the fifth month these measurements have increased to about ten inches in length and eleven ounces in weight. Hair has appeared on the head, and the outside of the body is covered with a fatty substance. The mother becomes conscious of movements in her uterus (womb), especially when she is resting quietly.

The fetus at six months is twelve to fourteen inches long and weighs from one to two pounds. Eyebrows and eyelashes have appeared, and in many ways it resembles a new-born baby. The child may survive for a few hours if born at this time, but rarely more than that.

A month later, at the seventh month, the weight of the fetus has increased to approximately three pounds and its length to about sixteen inches. It is still rather slender but will fill out considerably during its next two months.

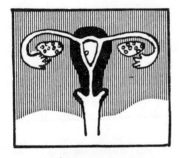

The inner lining of the uterus is the resting place for the fertilized egg, which begins to grow in size after attaching itself.

Growing and dividing very rapidly, the egg, within a month, is an embryo like that pictured at the left.

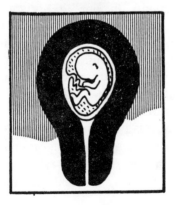

Within two months after the fertilized egg lodges itself, it is much bigger and already beginning to look like a baby.

A child has a fair chance of survival if born at this time or after.

The average baby at birth is about twenty inches long and about seven to seven and one-half pounds in weight. During the last two months of its fetal life it loses the fine hairs which covered the skin surface, and the skin becomes smooth but still reddish. The eyes have a blue cast to them, but at this stage, what their permanent color will be no one can predict. Fat tissue is being stored up under the skin, taking away the wrinkles. Most of the organs are functioning normally. This completes the history of pre-natal life. The baby is ready to be born.

How the Fetus Lives

We have observed the growth and development of the embryo and fetus from the beginning of pre-natal life, but have said nothing as yet regarding how life is sustained during its fetal growth. Provision must be made for the life of the baby within the mother, and God has so planned it that this need is wonderfully met.

When the fertilized embryo attaches itself to the lining of the uterus and the cluster of cells begins to multiply and grow, some of the cells form a placental sac which completely encloses the embryo. This sac grows along with the baby, and contains fluid in which the baby floats until birth. The sac and fluid protect the baby from jolts which might otherwise injure the tiny being. They also serve to regulate the temperature of its home. Thus the growing fetus is ideally situated, suspended in a shock-absorbing medium and at an even temperature.

How does the baby breathe while living in this fluid medium? Actually, it doesn't. The lungs of the unborn baby are not used during this time, for it receives its oxygen from the blood of its mother. The fetus is completely dependent, therefore, upon its mother's blood for life and growth. This fact adds new meaning to Leviticus 17:11, "The life of the flesh is in the blood," and to the New Testament emphasis upon the blood of Christ. In stressing the blood of Christ the New Testament highlights the life of Christ, which was offered for men.

Nourishment and oxygen for the fetus are provided through the placenta and umbilical cord. The placenta is a disk-shaped organ which develops on the wall of the uterus at the point where the ovum first lodged. The baby is joined to this placenta by a thick cord called the umbilical cord. It is attached to the center of the baby's abdomen on the other end, and this area is later known as the navel.

God has made the placenta an amazing filter. Food materials, oxygen and other substances necessary for the life of the baby are absorbed by the placenta from the blood vessels in the wall of the uterus in much the same way that water is absorbed through the roots of a plant. These vital materials are then channeled to the system of the fetus by the umbilical cord. Yet the membranes in the placenta prevent any of the impurities of the mother's blood from coming through. These are sifted out and disposed of. Waste materials including carbon dioxide from the baby's system, however, are able to pass back through the very same membranes and are eventually discharged with other impurities from the mother's system.

In all of this exchange of materials, the blood of the mother and the blood of the child never mix or unite. The baby is a separate being, even while living in direct dependence upon the mother's system in the uterus.

CHANGES IN THE MOTHER

It is not easy for a woman to detect pregnancy in its very early stages, but some changes take place in the mother soon after conception which serve as indications of what has happened within her. First of all, her menstrual periods cease. This sign is not conclusive, because other factors besides pregnancy can interrupt the monthly cycle. The woman may experience nausea or "morning sickness" before pregnancy is very far advanced; also an increased frequency of urination. Changes in the breasts provide another sign. The breasts become larger and more firm, and the nipples fill out; the area surrounding them becomes darker. None of these indicators is sufficient in itself to prove pregnancy, but a combination of several is strong evidence.

Scientific tests involving the injection of the woman's urine into a rabbit, mouse, or frog, have been devised which can with accuracy establish pregnancy, or lack of it, during the first month. The signs which nature alone provides are not discernible so soon.

Of course, the part of the mother which undergoes the most noticeable change is the abdomen. As the softened uterus stretches to accommodate the growing fetus, the whole abdominal wall expands proportionately. The increase is noted first in the lower part, but as the months pass the abdomen keeps on protruding until, after eight months, it has rounded out to the height of the ribs. A few weeks prior to birth, the baby settles down in the lower area of the abdomen, causing the bulge to become even more prominent.

Throughout pregnancy, the mother is especially conscious and careful of her health, knowing that the health and well-being of her baby are directly involved. She visits the doctor regularly, eats proper meals, and drinks quantities of water. Nights of sound sleep and afternoon naps are important. She may safely gain as much as twenty-five pounds in weight before delivery, but less is likely to prove advantageous. A certain amount of exercise is beneficial for her. In fact, many mothers feel especially well during pregnancy.

Some expectant mothers are superstitious concerning the effects of certain experiences during pregnancy upon their yet unborn children. Birthmarks and deformities cannot be caused by experiences of the mother. If a child is born with a red birthmark, the explanation is not that the mother was frightened by a fire engine during pregnancy. Nor can a well-meaning mother transmit artistic talent to her unborn child by cultivating the arts herself during pregnancy. Since there is no connection between the nervous systems and the blood systems of mother and fetus, there is no way of transmitting, just by maternal impressions, either personality traits or physical marks which are not originally in the genes.

The prospective father has an important contribution to make to the mother's welfare during this time. He can be understanding and loving and help to ease her responsibilities in the home. He can arrange to spend more time with her, making plans for the great event which will soon enrich both their lives. Anticipation of the baby's birth can serve to draw the husband and wife even closer to each other and to the Lord.

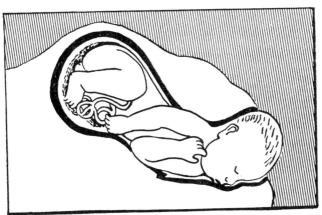

In the normal process of birth, the baby's head moves out of the mother first, as the muscle walls of the vagina expand to make room for the movement.

BIRTH OF THE BABY

After about forty weeks, or nine months of growth, the fetus is ready to leave its mother's womb and be born into the outer world. Two weeks or so before the onset of labor, the fetus shifts into the lower part of the pelvis area and begins to enter the birth canal, head first. When the mother begins to feel mild cramping sensations, much like menstrual cramps, she knows her time is near. These cramps are called "labor" and quite appropriately so, for the body must work hard to force the baby through the birth canal. At first these rhythmic sensations are brief and occur about every half hour or so. Gradually they become longer in duration and come at shorter intervals. Just before birth this muscular pressure occurs every minute or two.

The condition of the mother, her physical build, and her size help determine the length of time it will take her to give birth to her child. Usually the first child takes anywhere from five to twenty hours. Second and successive children are frequently delivered more quickly.

The mother is usually attended by a doctor and one or more nurses, whether she goes to the hospital or remains at home for her delivery. During the early stages of labor, and occasionally even before labor pains begin, the sac of fluid surrounding the baby bursts, notifying the mother and those attending her that the newcomer is soon to arrive.

Labor may be divided into three stages. In the first stage, the mother's organs prepare for the baby's exit. The pelvis expands, and the opening between the uterus and the vagina, that is, the cervix, dilates in order to permit the baby to pass through.

In the second stage, through the muscular contractions of uterus and vagina, the baby is expelled from the birth canal which has also expanded in order that the baby's head and body might pass through.

Of particular interest in this stage of the process is God's provision for the infant's head. Before birth, it is composed of three bony parts connected by flexible tissues. There are two soft spots called fontanels which allow for easier birth. Thus, the head can contract as it is forced through the narrow birth canal, without damaging the brain. Several months after birth, these parts fuse, the soft spot disappears, and the skull becomes permanently hard.

The doctor usually aids the mother through the more severe pains during the last stages of labor by administering an anesthetic. As the baby's head emerges, he also helps to ease the infant into the great outside world.

The third and final stage of labor is commonly referred to as "afterbirth" or placental expulsion. Once the baby is outside of its mother's body, the doctor completes the separation of mother and child by cutting the umbilical cord. To prevent bleeding he ties the cord at two places, one of which is right next to the baby's abdomen. Neither mother nor child feels any pain, because there are no nerves in the cord. In a few days, the stub of the cord on the baby's abdomen dries up and drops off. The small, round hollow left in the center of the baby's abdomen is known as the navel. Then, last of all, the whole placenta and the remains of the cord are discharged from the uterus by the same muscular contraction which sent forth the child. This completes the process of labor.

Babies have a way of notifying the world of their presence. The doctor, the nurses and the father, if he is near enough, are delighted to hear the youngster's first cry because this means that its lungs are working for the first time. Eyes are treated with a solution of silver nitrate, destroying any germs that might cause infection. Soon baby is ready for the nursery.

The mother will remain in bed resting for a few days. This allows her reproductive organs to return to

their normal size and function. Undoubtedly, she will feel tired at first, but the presence of her new son or daughter will cheer her. After two or three days, she will begin to produce milk from her breasts, and she may nurse her baby for several months. Both baby and mother should see their doctor regularly for several months after birth to check on their progress.

By the wonderful processes of mating, fertilization,

prenatal development and birth, God permits men to share in the creation of an immortal soul! But man's role is definitely secondary. With all of man's sophistication, with all of his ability to invent machines and to build empires, the creation of life — that dramatic and inconceivably ingenious achievement — is the prerogative of only One — our sovereign God!

Questions and Answers

How can a wife know if she is pregnant?
Nature provides some indications which show up in due time, such as the ceasing of menstruation, changes in the breasts, "morning sickness," frequent urination, etc. Laboratory tests can determine pregnancy within hours, by injecting the blood or urine of the woman into certain animals. If the woman is pregnant, the hormones in her blood or urine will bring about ovulation in the animal almost immediately. The Friedman test uses rabbits, the Ascheim-Zondek test, mice. A newly devised test uses frogs, because the results can be obtained more rapidly.

What makes a baby either a boy or a girl?
The sex of the baby is set at the moment of conception, and depends upon which type of sperm fertilized the egg cell. The testes of the father manufacture two types of sperm cells, one of which contains a chromosome for boys and the other for girls. Since these two types are produced in about equal quantities, it is a fifty-fifty chance whether the baby will be a boy or a girl.

Can parents learn the sex of their baby before it is born?
Not with any degree of certainty. Many of the supposed tests for ascertaining sex are undependable. Girls do not

cause their mothers to develop a preference for sweet foods, nor boys for sour foods. Boys do not cause their mothers more nausea than girls. Nor are boys necessarily carried high in the abdomen and girls low. All these ideas lack the foundation of fact. Even the difference between male and female heartbeat is not reliable because it is so relative.

How does a fetus breathe inside its mother?
Babies do not use their lungs at all during prenatal life. Rather, they receive their oxygen and nourishment from the mother's blood stream through the placenta and umbilical cord. Usually a baby's lungs first begin to function when, after it has been born, the doctor "spanks" it and makes it cry.

What is a miscarriage?
This is the discharge or birth of the fetus before it is sufficiently developed to survive. Most miscarriages occur during the second or third months of pregnancy. It is usually due to faulty structure or imperfect growth of the fetus. This is nature's way of stopping a pregnancy which probably could not be completed successfully.

The first symptom of miscarriage is usually bleeding from the vagina, often accompanied by abdominal cramps or pain. In such cases, a doctor should be consulted.

Shortly after a miscarriage the wife usually feels well, and is able to carry on her daily routine as usual.

What is a premature baby?
Babies born when they are able to survive outside of their mothers' bodies, but yet before the full term of pregnancy has been fulfilled, are called premature babies.

Because they are not yet ready for the outside world they must frequently be kept in incubators, where the temperature can be controlled as in the mother's womb.

Are great musicians born of mothers who took piano lessons during pregnancy?

Women who cultivate the arts during pregnancy may make something of the home environment which will affect the child after birth, but such activities cannot influence the fetus in prenatal life. By the same token, birthmarks and deformities, which very rarely occur, are not due to frightful experiences or shocks to the mother during pregnancy.

How does the mother know when she is ready to deliver her baby?

First of all, she knows the approximate date of the baby's arrival by figuring forty weeks from her last menstrual period. However, the baby may arrive before this forty week period is completed. The onset of labor can be detected by mild muscular contractions in the uterus and vagina. The sac surrounding the baby may burst and the fluid be discharged through the vagina. These are strong indications that delivery is near.

How long does labor last?

Sixteen hours is the average length of labor for first babies, about eleven hours for second and successive babies. Occasionally, a mother will be in labor for as much as thirty hours. A few are in labor for only three hours. However, with proper medical care, she may experience very little pain in giving birth to a child.

What is a Caesarean Section?

Some mothers are unable to deliver their babies through the birth canal. The pelvis may be too small, or the placenta may be covering the cervix. When this is true, the baby is delivered through the abdominal wall by a surgical operation known as a "Caesarean Section." It is so named because Julius Caesar is said to have been born this way.

What is a still-birth?

Once in a very great while a baby is born dead. This is called a "still-birth." It may be due to certain diseases which the mother communicates to the child or to an injury to the unborn baby or to its mother; or to a very hard birth. It may also be attributed to an anemic condition in the infant resulting from a conflict between differing Rh factors in mother and baby.

Does the bearing of a child impair a woman physically?

No! God has so constituted the woman that she is not harmed by bearing children. After the placenta and remainder of the cord have been expelled from the uterus, the woman's reproductive organs immediately begin to return to their normal size and function.

What happens to the baby of a "dry" mother?

Some mothers are not able to provide milk for their babies. Then the baby is fed from a bottle with a specially prepared formula.

Can a mother become pregnant again while she is still nursing?

The return of menstruation may be delayed for several months if a mother is nursing, but generally she is able to conceive again long before she ceases to nurse her baby.

Does a woman ruin her figure by breast feeding her baby?

No. In fact, some medical authorities state that breast feeding may result in the development of the breasts.

Can anything be done for a husband and wife who want children, but who do not seem to be able to have them?

Yes! Childless couples very frequently benefit from the services of a medical specialist such as a gynecologist, urologist, or endocrinologist. Professionally trained marriage counsellors and psychologists also render valuable service.

Can scientists produce fertilization artificially, that is, in a test tube?

No, and the prospects are highly unlikely, because the conditions which prevail inside the mother are apparently impossible to match. Undoubtedly, God permits this function to occur only as He has intended it.

8

Special Problems of Sex

There is scarcely a segment of human interest and activity that does not have some sexual considerations. Since sex is a vital, influential aspect of life which affects all areas of living, it is not surprising that many sex problems arise.

They may be attributed to the fact that people do not have a divine nature, and are without adequate wisdom to cope with all life situations. Hence, they may become seriously confused and maladjusted.

The best single preventative for sex problems is an early acceptance of Christ as Saviour, and constant reliance upon Him. God gives unerring wisdom to those who trust in Him. However, some Christians develop such problems because they follow Christ afar off, thereby refusing the wisdom which God so graciously offers. Still other believers develop or even contribute to these problems because their actions are not marked by common sense and thoughtfulness.

145

There are a number of sex problems such as masturbation, homosexuality and various sex complexes. Very often these difficulties are outward signs of inward disturbances, a lack of proper adjustment to life.

One thing is usually true about sex problems — people are not born with them. Sex problems are gradually acquired as a girl or boy grows up. Therefore, if wrong patterns are to be avoided, wholesome sex education is important. Understanding the cause of the problem and its effect on our bodies and minds not only proves to be a necessary step to their elimination, but is often an effective preventative.

It is impossible to secure reliable statistics about the unnatural in sex. Some men and women will not discuss their personal problems. Others enjoy talking about sex, getting a second-hand thrill out of recounting sex adventures which may or may not be true. But this much is certain, anything that affects every member of society as much as sex does, is bound to result in a number of problems.

MASTURBATION

In all probability, the most common sex problem is masturbation. Masturbation may be defined as self-stimulation of the genital organs in order to achieve sexual release and gratification. It is a concern of boys and girls as well as adults. The percentages are no doubt highest among boys and unmarried men, partially due to the fact that the male sex organs are external to the body and that the male is usually sexually aroused or excited more quickly than the female.

The very mention of the word masturbation customarily brings forth an adverse reaction. "Musn't touch!

Nasty, nasty!" are common expressions. No doubt such adult actions are an effort to frighten young people out of their bad habits. But fright, rather than wise advice, is not the answer. It often has the effect of making a person conceal his wrong-doing.

There are many erroneous ideas on the subject. While in no sense of the word can the following be construed as justifying the practice of masturbation, nevertheless, the facts should be faced. It is not the shocking, filthy habit that it is often thought to be. Neither is it necessarily a sign of perversion nor moral corruption. Contrary to common belief, masturbation does not cause insanity, feeble-mindedness, sexual impotency or sterility, or stunted growth. It is not responsible for facial blemishes, dark circles around the eyes or a foreboding cast to the eyes. It has very few, if any, proven physically damaging effects.

People differ greatly in their beliefs concerning the ill effects of continued masturbation. Undoubtedly the most common is the feeling of guilt. Guilt feelings prevent one from being his best. It may keep him from making effective social adjustments. It robs him of a most valuable possession, "a conscience void of offense toward God and man" (Acts 24:16). Furthermore, most people who regularly practice masturbation seriously regret their lack of self control.

Masturbation is sometimes practiced by children, adolescents and adults, and must be interpreted variously for each of the three groups.

CHILDHOOD

Manipulation of the genital organs during early childhood may have little sexual significance. Every child is an explorer, learning about himself and his world largely through the sense of touch. With no intent to bring about erotic sensation, all small children do a certain amount of handling of their sex organs. In its milder forms, this is not serious and should be ignored. When parents deal understandingly with this behavior, it will usually disappear naturally.

Complications arise when the parent makes an unnecessary issue over the behavior. As, for instance, in the case of four-year-old Johnny. He awakened early one morning and lay idly in bed. With nothing to take his attention, he found an outlet in examining and handling himself. When his mother entered the room she caught him "in the act." She manifested shock and disapproval, exclaiming that he was very bad and would never grow to be tall and strong if he continued such practices. He was to be spanked if she ever caught him again. Her reaction to the act added importance to it. Thus it became something worth doing again.

The added sense of guilt might do considerable damage to the child's personality development. Such a cure may be worse than the difficulty itself. Anxiety and a feeling of unworthiness undermine a child's self-confidence and make it difficult for him to achieve a healthy, happy outlook on life.

If a child is made to feel guilty or ashamed of his behavior, then real complications could easily develop. This would make the true causes more difficult to reach, because the person would not feel free to discuss them if they were covered by guilt feelings.

ADOLESCENCE

Among adolescents, masturbation is almost always a consciously sexual act. The years between puberty and marriage are difficult years for the adolescent. The intensity of the fully developed sex drive varies from individual to individual. Some suffer but little discomfort in this adjustment period. Others, perhaps the majority, find it very hard to regulate their insistent sex impulse. Masturbation is one way of gaining immediate release from sexual tensions. It is resorted to by some simply because it is a physical outlet without a partner, thus avoiding social complications.

Added to these physical urges are the abundance of off-color jokes, stories and pictures which circulate in many schools. Adolescents are approaching something new in life, which naturally arouses their curiosity. The lewd-minded give them fuel for their curiosity in the form of exciting half-truths. All too often these half-truths comprise most of the sex knowledge of a young person. No one is helping him to think clearly. The jokes, the insinuating laughter result in unhealthy stimulation, unwholesome attitudes — often exploratory masturbation.

When physical desire and lewd thinking are the causes, the answer to the problem is to be found in a stronger allegiance to Christ. Christians should realize, "There hath no temptation taken you but such as is common to man: but God is faithful, who will not suffer you to be tempted above that ye are able; but will with the temptation also make a way to escape, that ye may be able to bear it" (I Corinthians 10:13).

A realization that others face this temptation and

yet have victory over it should give a young person the confidence that he too can have victory through Christ.

The key to overcoming temptation is partly in the control of the mind. It is true that sex drives are physical, but they are intensified by constantly thinking about them. A desire to be a cleaner, more usable, vessel for the Master will enable one to obey the injunction, "present your bodies a living sacrifice, holy, acceptable unto God, which is your reasonable service." (Romans 12:1).

Masturbation is sometimes the sign of emotional stress and strain. Something in the home or at school may be making the fellow or girl tense and worried. These deeper causes need to be identified and eliminated before the symtomatic behavior will pass away. *Here is something which is true of nearly all sex problems: they are symptoms of deeper personality problems.*

All too often, the teen-ager turns to masturbation because it is a form of compensation. In other words, it seemingly takes the place of a basic need which is not being met in his life. If he can't find satisfaction elsewhere, he'll find it by himself.

Larry experienced difficulty making friends at school. He was in few activities, and he felt that even his teachers didn't have time for him. At home his family life had always been hectic and filled with tension. His parents were on the verge of divorce, and neither of them seemed to care what happened to him. As a consequence, Larry masturbated considerably in secret. It was his way of feeling sorry for himself and finding comfort. Being rejected at home and at school, self gratification became important to him.

Larry's greatest need was to be in a Christian home.

If his parents could forget their own selfish clashes and think of their responsibility to their son, and make a happy Christian home, the temptation to masturbate would probably have disappeared.

The first step, and in many cases a sufficient one, is for the boy or girl to be led into a right relationship with Christ. At the time of spiritual conversion, one receives a new nature, new power, a new outlook — in fact, "All things are become new." However, devoted Christians may benefit from human assistance. Here, a pastor or a young people's worker is of the utmost help. He can assist the young person in establishing a regular schedule of Bible study and prayer and encourage him to take a more active part in various Christian activities. A sympathetic adult can counsel and guide the young fellow or girl into understanding and solving his problem. In case after case, it has been found that when a boy or girl acknowledges the problem of masturbation to a Christian and discusses it fully, the difficulty disappears.

One gains psychological support by sharing a problem with another. If the adolescent has a close friend about his own age with whom he can discuss the problem, the "sharing" lessens the weight of it and the troubled person finds release in discussion instead of masturbation. The association of a good Christian pal is always an effective deterrent to masturbation because of the inspiration which is afforded, rather than the undue and unwholesome stimulation regarding sex matters.

Dates, too, are a natural outlet and help clear up the condition. One might think that because of the physical nearness involved in dates, they would increase the problem. But on the contrary since they are a normal, wholesome activity, the result is to lessen the tendency to masturbate.

An additional contributing factor to continued masturbation is ignorance regarding the human body, especially of sexual functions. After a boy or a girl has carefully studied the human body, and has gained an understanding of the sex organs and their marvelous functions, there follows a greater measure of profound respect for sex matters. This is an important factor in overcoming masturbation.

In a few instances medical examinations might reveal skin irritation or certain other conditions which need attention. Cleanliness of the genital region and properly fitting clothes should also be taken into consideration.

ADULTHOOD

As age advances, if the practice of masturbation continues, it may become more serious. It may lead to one's becoming maladjusted socially, preferring his own company and his own manipulated sex releases. It may also interfere with a person's ability to make a good sex adjustment in marriage.

A person who masturbates over a period of time conditions himself to respond sexually in a manner which is in conflict with normal husband and wife relations. Masturbation is based upon selfishly satisfying one's own self rather than pleasing the marriage partner, thus damage may be done to the person's normal relationship.

The desire to overcome habitual masturbation must begin with each individual. He must recognize his problem and sincerely want to do something about it. Once the desire is awakened, then all of the previous suggestions will help: sex education, normal social activity, fulfillment of basic emotional needs, possible medical attention, wise use of leisure time, frank discussions, counselling sessions, spiritual conversion, participation in Christian activities, and wholesome associations with a Christian pal. But the greatest help is having a deep, personal relationship with the Lord Jesus Christ. He is the inexhaustible source of strength for those who trust Him. One should not wait until all else has failed before turning to Christ. He must be made the absolute pivot in one's life. God's power to help people with their individual and personal problems is beyond comprehension! He has promised, "All power is given unto me in heaven and in earth . . . and, lo, I am with you alway, even unto the end of the world" (Matthew 28:18 and 20). He will surely guide those who come unto Him!

HOMOSEXUALITY

Bob seldom dates girls. He seems to think of them more as sisters. In fact, he even acts much like a girl himself. Bob has a boy friend, but the two act more like "dates" than pals. Whenever they get a chance at night, they go places, then sleep together. Although Bob is a young adult, he has a serious "crush" on his boy friend. The two fellows secretly engage in unwholesome and unnatural sex-play with each other.

Bob has been doing this for some time, not only with his special friend, but with several other boys who live in the neighboring communities. Bob has reached a point where he receives a great deal of enjoyment from this sex activity with his few homosexual friends. He has considerable scholastic ability, makes good grades, but he is really not happy. He knows that he is unlike the other boys, and he finds it more and more difficult to act in a normal masculine fashion. In fact, he is always quietly on the lookout for another boy with whom he might have homosexual relations. Several boys, younger than himself, have been approached, and two or three of them, not knowing what they were getting into, have gone along with Bob and are now being introduced to homosexuality.

So Bob's problem continues, a clandestine affair, damaging his own life as well as those of the other boys with whom he has come into contact. He cannot help himself, mainly because he does not know how. He is afraid to go to anyone with his problem because he is certain that anyone who isn't a homosexual will be shocked and disgusted with him. He knows that if it were suspected, he would be ostracized and possibly reported to the police. And so he goes on and on, building up reactions that in time bind him closer to the perversion. He needs someone to understand him so that he may come to understand himself.

"Homo" means the same, and "homosexual" means attracted to the same sex. Overt homosexuality involves actual contact with a member of the same sex in some sort of sexual behavior. Latent homosexuality is characterized by a strong preference for the members of the same sex without direct expression of that preference in a physical act. In either case, homosexuality is considered abnormal when it is the preferred type of sexual adjustment.

There is no way of accurately estimating the number of homosexuals in our society. Comparatively few are going to declare themselves, in the face of society's disapproval. Even so, it is a known fact that there are many, many thousands.

Contrary to popular concept, there are no physical characteristics by which to recognize homosexuals. Certain traits, such as a high-pitched voice, well-developed breasts, and feminine distribution of body hair, are thought to be common to all male homosexuals, but this is not the case. Neither is it true that all male homosexuals are effeminate in interests and behavior. Some of the traits which are thought to characterize homosexuals are characteristic of people who are not homosexuals, and vice versa. In fact, a study of the physical measurements of a group of male homosexuals showed that they do not differ markedly in physique from typical college or army men. Nor are homosexual women (lesbians) physically different from other women.

People, whether male or female, are basically people. All men are much like women, just as all women are much like men. Although they are basically different, they are basically alike. No man is all man; no woman is all woman. All men and women are first of all people having many similarities. However, God has created men for sex roles which are distinctly masculine, and He has intended that women assume sex roles which are feminine. It is the departure from this normal pattern that creates the problem.

When the subject of homosexuality is discussed, it should be remembered that all children pass through a time of growth and development when they prefer being with their own gang of the same sex. That is a normal part of growing up. Most young girls have had, at one time or another, a "crush" on a highly-respected teacher or older woman. Such relationships are not signs or symptoms of homosexuality, but are natural, and they will disappear as they pass through that particular phase of growth and development.

There are several theories for the cause of homosexuality. It has been suggested that it is an inherited tendency. Studies have indicated that this has only been true in less than one percent of the cases studied. Another theory suggests that homosexuality is prompted by lack of balance of the sex hormones in the system. This theory is plausible because it is true that both males and females have in their systems hormones of the opposite sex. Experimentally, however, while it was found that some homosexuals showed lack of balance, many did not.

There is far greater substantial evidence that conditioning and environmental factors are responsible for homosexuality. There is general agreement as to the superiority of this theory.

Children may accidentally slip into homosexual practices. When those of the same sex sleep together because of crowded home conditions, erotic bodily contact may result. The mutual gratification throws the two together and attachments are deepened. Eventually they defend their actions and build up a faulty behavior pattern which could be lasting and harmful.

Sometimes homosexual practices occur when boys or girls are placed in military and boarding schools where there is rather strict segregation. Their bodies are developing, physical urges are strong, so they pick up sex information and gain some pleasure through mutual stimulation and sex play. Too, an adolescent in such a situation may be lonesome, and especially susceptible to unwholesome relationships. The vicious circle of practice, and defense by repetition can result in a maladjusted person.

It is important that normal social relationships between boys and girls be developed during adolescence. Sometimes wrong instruction or lack of instruction in matters of sex may cause the adolescent to shy away from wholesome boy-girl contacts, and thus seek homosexual relationships.

In some cases, having been unkindly treated by the parent of the opposite sex has resulted in antagonism toward that sex, and a homosexual pattern begins. Even too strong an attachment to a parent of the same sex may encourage the development of homosexual tendencies. Jane's parents separated when she was quite young. Her mother monopolized Jane's affection, turning her against men, with the result that Jane was comfortable only in the company of women.

Marital conflict between parents may sour a child on heterosexual (boy-girl) relationships in general. Mildred, who came from a very unhappy home, had many personality problems. She never seemed to "click" with people. She thought of herself as unworthy, incapable and unwanted. She was not a Christian. In college she made friends with another girl who had a strong, dominant personality. Mildred attached herself to her college friend, and before long found herself engaged in sex activities with her. As the years went on the girls became more and more involved in homosexuality, until at graduation time, Mildred had no interest in dating boys. She was happiest when she and another girl or two would take a room for a week-end and engage in unnatural sex acts. Mildred is now employed professionally, but she is a social misfit. She is a homosexual who finds no satisfaction in ordinary associations with either sex, except when she has sex relations with a few other girls. She is quite successful at hiding her serious problem, and only a limited number of people know her true condition. But as she grows older, the problem grows more acute, and she attempts more and more to justify her condition.

Another cause of homosexuality is the attitude of some parents toward their children. They want a girl but get a boy, or vice versa, and treat the child as if he were the sex they wanted. Such treatment casts the child into the wrong sex role and after playing the part for years, he finds it difficult to react as he should. Such was the case of Bernice. Her father wanted a boy, so for years he treated her as one. Later she went to Hollywood and became the sex companion of a middle-aged alcoholic woman. Inwardly, Bernice defied the world, demanding that she be accepted as she was.

A defiant attitude may be one reason why the Bible calls homosexuality sin. For the Bible does speak strongly of it as sin, saying:

> Wherefore God also gave them up to uncleanness through the lusts of their own hearts, to dishonour their own bodies between themselves:
> Who changed the truth of God into a lie, and worshipped and served the creature more than the Creator, who is blessed for ever. Amen.
> For this cause God gave them up unto vile affections: for even their women did change the natural use into that which is against nature:

And likewise also the men, leaving the natural use of the woman, burned in their lust one toward another; men with men working that which is unseemly, and receiving in themselves that recompence of their error which was meet.

And even as they did not like to retain God in their knowledge, God gave them over to a reprobate mind, to do those things which are not convenient; (Romans 1:24-28).

Homosexual practices are wrong. But equally wrong is the demand on the part of homosexuals that their perversion be accepted as normal. Some homosexuals do not want help. They are defiant in their attitude toward God and man, demanding that society accept the misfits, which they are, as if they were normal. Society cannot do this, although it must seek to help them.

In order to help the homosexual, one has to learn to look at him as a person with a personality or a "life" problem. The homosexual needs help with his feelings, his outlook, his frustrations. It should again be repeated that the homosexual is not born that way. People, circumstances, environment and experiences have made him as he is. Therefore, he can be helped.

Marriage is not a sure cure. Getting married may be a step in the direction of rehabilitation, but simply getting married does not cure the personality maladjustment. Psychological treatment of the right kind, through study of the individual, his attitudes and feelings, will help the homosexual.

However, salvation and dynamic Christian living are the most effective cures for the homosexual. A right relationship to Christ makes this unique and important contribution toward overcoming homosexuality — it causes the homosexual to want to change! While formerly demanding society to accept his homosexuality as normal, wanting his perverted behavior legalized, now, through the Spirit of God, he wants to change. This is the first step in rehabilitation! When the Holy Spirit indwells a man there is a great resource of power. "For God hath not given us the spirit of fear, but of power" (II Timothy 1:7).

It is especially significant that Paul deals with homosexuality in I Corinthians 6:9. Then in the eleventh verse he says, "And such were some of you," indicating that there were some in the Corinthian church who had been characterized by homosexual traits. However, Paul declared that through Christ they were no longer so: ". . . But ye are washed, but ye are sanctified, but ye are justified in the name of the Lord Jesus, and by the Spirit of our God."

When a person is busily engaged serving the Lord, praying, studying the Bible, leading others to Christ and experiencing fellowship with other believers, though he may have a problem of this sort, he is well on the way to normal adjustment.

SEX COMPLEXES

Many are the sex complexes that beset human beings. When a person has an abnormal preoccupation with the things of sex, it may be described as a sex complex. Such complexes vary with the individual.

Everyone gives some thought to sex. Outside stimuli provoke such thoughts. Glands within arouse emotion. A certain amount of thought about sex is accepted as a normal part of living, but, a person with a sex complex is one whose consciousness is so persistently dominated by such thinking that it becomes a controlling factor in his life, keeping him from being a balanced, happy individual. Fred had reached a point in his sex complex that he imagined the minister could read it in his eyes, and often, in the midst of a sermon, he would get up and walk out of church. He was unable to live a normal life because he could not look at people, for fear they would "see the sex in his eyes."

When not corrected, a person with a sex complex reaches the point where he imagines improbable and unnatural things. He may think that people are saying things of a sex nature about him. He may project sexual meaning into ordinary objects and events.

A sex complex may become sufficiently serious that one should seek professional psychological or psychiatric help in order to live a normal life. As with other problems of sex, the road to improvement usually calls for an understanding of the causes, proper sex education, channeling activities and tensions into worthwhile projects, wholesome contacts with those of the opposite sex, sympathetic counsel of parents, professional help, Christian friends and spiritual assistance.

However, the best preventative against sex problems is an early acceptance of Christ as Saviour and consistent Christian living throughout one's lifetime.

God makes definite promises in His Word to the one who receives Christ as Saviour and comes to Him for help. He pledges: "Thou wilt keep him in perfect peace, whose mind is stayed on thee; because he trusteth in thee" (Isaiah 26:3). This is the guidance of God, in contrast to the stumbling way of perversion. As the Christian walks in the way of the Lord, He establishes his going. One should never underestimate the power of God, but give himself fully "unto him that is able to keep you from falling, and to present you faultless before the presence of his glory with exceeding joy" (Jude 24).

VENEREAL DISEASES

Two of the most common diseases are syphilis and gonorrhea. Although they are separate diseases, they are both contracted through sexual contact with an infected person. Both can become serious, but there is a cure for them. Infected persons should consult a private physician, or a local health clinic.

It is impossible by looking at a person to know whether he has such a disease. The best protection is restricting sexual intercourse to marriage. Most states require a premarital examination of both bride and groom in order to determine the presence of venereal infection.

SYPHILIS

Syphilis is generally acquired through sexual intercourse with an infected person. However, it can be caught by an unborn baby from the mother. If the mother has been adequately treated during early pregnancy, the disease can be prevented from affecting the child.

In its primary stage, syphilis is characterized by a sore called *chancre* which usually appears on the genitals. Later there may be symptoms of sore throat, skin rash and headaches.

In its more advanced stage, the symptoms may reappear as much as twenty years after the initial infection. The reason for this is that after the *chancre* disappears, the germs pass into the blood stream where they remain quiescent.

Syphilis may attack any part of the body, including the heart, and the nervous system. If concentrated in the brain, these germs may result in insanity and paralysis. This dread disease has also been known to leave disfiguring sores, blindness and other incapacities. Detection of syphilis may be made by blood tests.

GONORRHEA

Gonorrhea is probably the most common of venereal diseases. Infection usually results from sexual intercourse with one who has the disease. Infection caused otherwise is not so common. It may be acquired in babies by means of a nurse or mother who already has the infection, and who is not careful to wash her hands before caring for the infant.

Symptoms in the male are those of itching and burning at the opening of the penis. This is usually accompanied by a thick, yellowish discharge. These symptoms commonly appear about three days after exposure.

In the female, the symptoms are also that of burning and itching of the urethra. This is accompanied by a yellowish discharge. The symptoms may be more easily overlooked in a woman, but the after effects may become very serious.

Fortunately, these serious complications can usually be avoided by prompt and thorough treatment by competent medical doctors using effective medicines. The eyes of new-born babies are usually protected from possible gonorrheal infection of the mother by placing a solution in the baby's eyes at the time of birth.

Venereal infection is unlikely except in sexual intercourse with an infected person. Most localities have clinics where low cost treatment is available, thereby affording a cure if cared for soon after infection. And yet it is unfortunate that although there are many facilities for handling venereal diseases, the incidence of such diseases is still significant.

PREVENTING CONCEPTION

The prevention of conception is commonly known as birth control, or contraception. The term is applied either to the removal of factors which cause conception, or to the use of diaphragms, contraceptives, and other devices which prevent live male sperm cells from entering the womb. Contraception prevents the possible formation of new life, but it does not interfere with new life after it has begun.

As indicated elsewhere, fertilization is possible during a relatively short period of each month. Even during this period, no sperm may be able to penetrate the egg cell. Hence, not every act of sexual intercourse results in pregnancy.

Matters pertaining to birth control are of a personal concern to each husband and wife. They are also concerns of some religious groups, especially the Roman Catholic Church. Naturally, birth control has medical aspects, since various methods are prescribed by competent physicians.

Questions and Answers

What do problems of sex often indicate?
Sex problems are seldom that and only that. More frequently they are symtoms of deeper personality problems. The causes behind sex problems are many and complex.

Is it abnormal to have thoughts about sex?
God has made sex a normal, integral part of life. Thoughts regarding sex are a natural part of living.

However, if a person's preoccupations with sex matters prevent him from living a happy, successful life, such engrossment is abnormal.

If one has been truly born again and is intent on the things of Christ, he will find that God gives control of the mind, and remarkable freedom from unduly disturbing thoughts of a sexual nature.

What is a sex complex?
It is a group of emotionally toned sex attitudes, desires, or memories which in disguised form exerts a dominating influence upon the personality. One who has a sex complex usually has an abnormal preoccupation with sexual matters and thoughts, wherein non-sexual things arouse sexual associations.

Can masturbation stunt growth or cause one to become insane?

Research studies do not indicate such conclusions. There are many superstitions about such things, but they are without basis in fact. Masturbation does not cause insanity, stunted growth, physical deformities, facial blemishes, or the inability to have children.

What effect does masturbation have on later married life?

Individuals differ greatly in their beliefs concerning the ill effects of continued masturbation upon later married life. Perhaps the most commonly reported such effects are (a) regrets concerning lack of self control, (b) guilt feelings, and (c) the establishment of stimulation and response patterns which may be in conflict with those of normal sexual relations in marriage.

Is a person who masturbates considered a homosexual?

No, masturbation may have no relationship whatsoever to homosexuality.

What is homosexuality?

Homosexuality is characterized by inordinate sexual attraction toward individuals of the same sex, or active sexual relations between individuals of the same sex.

Homosexuality usually implies a continued preference for sexual relations with one or more members of the same sex, as well as a varying degree of rejection toward relations with the opposite sex.

What are some of the environmental factors which might be significant in causing a person to develop homosexual tendencies?

Lack of adequate sex education, lack of wholesome contact with members of the other sex, a strong attachment to the parent of the same sex, a strong dislike for the parent of the opposite sex, strong parental desire for a child of a different sex, shyness and early failure to adjust to playmates of the opposite sex, pleasurable initial homosexual experiences, unmet basic personality needs, lack of close friendships, and lack of a constant reliance on Christ.

Can a homosexual be cured?

Yes, there is definite help for people with homosexual traits. One of the most important factors is the person's own awareness of the problem and his desire to do something about it. Such a person can benefit from professional help.

The greatest dynamic in the rehabilitation of homosexuals is vital Christianity. First, a homosexual needs to accept Christ as his personal Saviour. When the Holy Spirit indwells a man, a great resource of power is brought into action. Many former homosexuals have stated that until they knew Christ, they had no desire to change.

Furthermore, rehabilitation is made easier if a person is busily engaged serving the Lord, praying, studying the Bible, leading others to Christ, and fellowshiping with believers.

What is meant by sublimation?

It is the channeling of sex energies into outlets which have nothing directly to do with sex, but which are socially approved outlets. Many people have found the solution to sexual tensions by expending energies in sports, dramatics, social and church activities. The person who is busy winning friends to Christ will find he has much better control of such tensions and urges.

Can a person be a devoted Christian and yet have serious sex problems?

Yes. Salvation is not dependent upon freedom from maladjustments, but rather, upon acknowledging one's sinful nature and accepting Christ as his personal Saviour. However, since most sex problems are life problems, salvation and dynamic Christian living are of utmost importance in prevention as well as rehabilitation. Christian living is life at its happiest, its fullest, its best!

How are venereal diseases contracted?

They may be contracted through sexual intercourse with an infected person, or from other contacts with an infected person. A baby may contract a venereal disease before birth from an infected mother.

9

Definitions

Part I — Anatomical Terms

ABDOMEN

That part of the trunk of the body found between the chest and legs; it contains the stomach, intestines and other organs including the internal sex organs.

ABORTION

Loss of the fetus from the uterus before it is able to live outside its mother's body, that is, before the twenty-sixth to the twenty-eighth week of growth. Abortions are of three types: spontaneous or accidental, criminally induced, and therapeutic. Spontaneous abortion is sometimes referred to as a miscarriage.

ACQUIRED TRAIT

A characteristic gained by an individual from his environment.

ADOLESCENCE

The period of life between childhood and adulthood commonly called youth (about 13-20 for males, about 12-19 for females); the time when marked physical changes occur in boys and girls, indicating that they are maturing into young men and women.

ADULT

A fully-grown and physically matured man or woman.

ADULTERY

Sexual intercourse between a married and an unmarried person, or between two married persons not wedded to each other; illicit sex relations.

AFTERBIRTH

The expulsion of placenta, cord and fetal membranes from the uterus directly after the baby has been born; the third and final stage of labor.

AMNION

Inner layer of the sac in which the fetus develops.

AMNIOTIC FLUID

The fluid in which the fetus is suspended within the amniotic sac.

ANATOMY

The science of the structure of the body and the relation of its parts.

ANESTHETIC

An agent or drug which deadens pain.

ASCHEIM-ZONDEK TEST

A scientific test for pregnancy in which the woman's blood or urine is injected into a mouse. If the woman is truly pregnant, the special hormones of pregnancy which are in her blood or urine will bring on rapid ovulation artificially in the mouse. Similar tests using rabbits and frogs have been devised.

BIRTH

The fact of being born; the process whereby the baby leaves its mother's body and enters the outside world.

BIRTH CANAL

The passage through which the child is born; includes cervix, vagina and vulva.

BIRTH CONTROL

Regulation of the birth rate by controlling conception; applied either to the removal of factors which cause conception, or to the use of diaphragms, contraceptives and other devices which prevent male sperm from entering the womb.

CAESAREAN SECTION

A surgical operation whereby a baby is delivered through an incision in the walls of the abdomen and uterus.

CELIBACY

State of being unmarried; singleness.

CERVIX

The neck of the uterus which expands to permit the baby to enter into the vagina and finally into the outer world.

CHROMOSOME

A microscopic, rodlike structure found in the cells. It carries the genes or units which cause family resemblances to be transferred from parent to child and which determine physical characteristics. Each body cell contains 48 chromosomes, except the sex cells (sperm and ovum) which contain 24 chromosomes each.

CIRCUMCISION

An operation performed on boys (usually when babies), removing the foreskin or loose flesh which covers the end of the penis.

CLITORIS

The highly sensitive organ just inside the front and upper end of the vulva, covered by a movable fold of skin; the center of sexual excitement in the female.

COITUS

Sexual intercourse; the union of the penis and the vagina.

COLOSTRUM

The liquid secreted by the mother's breasts just before and a few days after the birth of the child. Her real milk usually does not start to flow until two or three days after the birth.

CONCEPTION

Fertilization of the ovum by the sperm; inception; the moment a woman becomes pregnant due to the union of sperm and ovum within her body.

CONGENITAL TRAIT

A characteristic acquired by an individual before birth, but not inherited through the genes; a trait acquired by a child from its mother during pregnancy or birth. For example, a child may be born with a disease contracted from its mother during prenatal life.

CONTRACEPTION

Prevention of conception.

COORDINATION

The smooth, harmonious working together of the muscles of the body.

CORD

The rope-like structure which connects the fetus to the placenta; the umbilical cord.

COURTSHIP
The events and relationships leading up to, but not necessarily reaching marriage.

CYTOPLASM
The jelly-like inner part or living substance of a cell, exclusive of the nucleus; protoplasm.

DUCT GLANDS
The oil and sweat glands primarily, since their excretion is carried to the skin surface by ducts; glands that have external excretion.

EGG CELL
The female sex cell or ovum; when this cell has been penetrated by the male sex cell (sperm), a human embryo is conceived.

EJACULATION
The discharge of seminal fluid from the penis; an emission.

EMBRYO
A new life in its earliest stages; in human beings, a "baby" less than three months in prenatal development, growing inside its mother.

ENDOCRINE
The system of glands which secretes substances called hormones into the blood stream. Example: pituitary, testes, ovaries.

ERECTION
The rushing of blood into the penis, causing the tissues to swell and making the penis enlarged and rigid. This condition is necessary for the discharge of sperm cells from the body of the male.

EXCRETION

Waste substances expelled from the body; the process of excreting such substances.

FALLOPIAN TUBES

Tubes extending from the uterus to each ovary. The tubes are connected with the uterus, but not directly with the ovaries. They form the passageway for ova from the ovaries to the uterus, and fertilization usually takes place in one of the tubes.

FEMININE

Like, or of a woman; having the qualities of a woman; belonging to the female sex.

FERTILE

Capable of producing or reproducing life. An egg cell is fertile when it has united with a sperm cell. Men and women are fertile when they are able to have children.

FERTILIZATION

The act or process of becoming fertile; the joining of an egg cell and a sperm cell, producing a human embryo. Fertilization takes place within the mother's body.

FETUS

A fully developed embryo; an unborn child which usually has been in its mother's uterus at least three months.

FORESKIN

The cap of skin over the tip of the penis; that which is removed by circumcision; the prepuce.

FORNICATION

Sexual intercourse between two unmarried people.

FRATERNAL TWINS

Unlike twins; those who develop from two separate fertilized eggs. They may be of the same or the opposite sex.

FRIGIDITY

An abnormal aversion to sexual intercourse; the inability of a woman to experience sexual pleasures or gratification during intercourse (a condition which usually may be remedied).

GAMETE

A sex or reproductive cell of either male or female.

GENE

A tiny chemical unit which makes up a chromosome and which determines the physical characteristics of the body. Genes carry the family resemblances from the parents to the children.

GENITALS

The sex organs or reproductive organs, especially those on the outside of the body.

GESTATION

Pregnancy.

GLAND

An organ which secretes or excretes chemical substance. The endocrine glands secrete hormones into the blood stream. One of these, the pituitary gland, affects the rate of body growth. There are other glands in the body besides the endocrine glands. The sweat glands, for instance, help to regulate the temperature of the body.

GROWTH

Multiplication of the cells and development of the body in size, weight, and other features; the process of becoming adult.

GYNECOLOGIST

A physician who specializes in women's diseases.

HARLOT

A lewd woman; a prostitute.

HEREDITY

The transmission of physical and personality traits from parents to children through the genes of the cells.

HETEROSEXUAL

Interested in the opposite sex, as distinguished from homosexual.

HOMOSEXUAL

Interested in members of one's own sex. There are two types of homosexuals: *latent* homosexuals are able to suppress and control their sex interests in members of their own gender; *overt* homosexuals are those who actually enter into sex practices with others of their same sex.

HORMONE

Any chemical substances formed in the endocrine glands, which affect the activity or growth of another gland or some part of the body.

HYMEN

The membrane which covers, or partly covers, the opening of the vagina in most young girls. Its absence does not necessarily prove lack of virginity.

IDENTICAL TWINS

Twins which develop from a single fertilized ovum which has split in two. They look almost alike and are of the same sex.

IMPOTENCY

Sexual inadequacy in the male, corresponding to frigidity in the female.

INHERITED TRAIT

A characteristic transmitted to a child from its parents by way of the genes; hereditary trait.

LABOR

The rhythmical muscular movements of the uterus as it forces the baby out of the birth canal in child-bearing.

LACTATION

The secretion of milk from the mother's breasts to feed her baby.

MAIN SPERM DUCT

The vas deferens tube which conducts the sperm cells from their storage places in the scrotum to the penis. Each testis has one such duct.

MAMMARY GLANDS

The milk-producing glands located within the breasts of women.

MASCULINE

Like, or of a man; having the qualities of a man; belonging to the male sex.

MASTURBATION

The handling and stimulation of the genital organs in order to receive sexual pleasure.

MATING

The union of male and female in the reproductive act; the injection of the penis into the vagina, so that the sperm cells can be deposited.

MATURITY

Adulthood; the state of being fully grown and developed.

MENOPAUSE

The period of life for women, generally in the middle or late forties, when menstruation ceases.

MENSTRUATION

The normal flow of blood from the uterus through the vagina, occurring once a month for most women (from the Latin, *menstraus,* "monthly").

MISCARRIAGE

The loss of the embryo or fetus before it is old enough to live, between the first and sixth month of its growth in the womb.

MOTOR SKILLS

Ability to control muscles and bodily movements; muscular coordination.

NAVEL

The place in a person's abdomen where he was joined to the umbilical cord during prenatal life.

NUCLEUS

The vital center of a cell containing the chromosomes.

OBSTETRICIAN

A physician who specializes in taking care of women during pregnancy and who delivers babies.

OVARIES

The two almond-shaped reproductive glands of the female. They produce egg cells (ova) and certain hormones which have to do with the female's sex functioning and with the development of feminine body characteristics.

OVULATION

The shedding of eggs from the ovaries; the production of ripe ova.

OVUM

The female reproductive cell; the egg cell. The egg develops into an embryo when penetrated by a sperm cell.

PEDIATRICIAN

A physician who specializes in the care of young children from the time of birth until they are a few years old.

PELVIS

The structure of bones supporting the trunk of the body and through which a baby must pass at birth.

PENIS

The male sex organ through which sperm cells leave the body; also used to discharge urine.

"PERIOD"

The several days during each month when a woman menstruates; the period when her ovaries are shedding ripe ova; the menstrual period.

PETTING

To fondle and caress one of the opposite sex.

PHYSIOLOGY

The study of the constitution and functioning of the body.

PIGMENT

The substance in the body cells which gives coloring to the eyes, hair and skin.

PITUITARY

The small gland which secretes various hormones, including the growth hormone. It is located at the base of the brain.

PLACENTA

The structure formed in the lining of the uterus during pregnancy to provide for the nourishment of the fetus and for the disposal of its body wastes. It is expelled after delivery, becoming the afterbirth.

PORE

Tiny opening in the skin through which perspiration passes.

PREGNANT

Condition of a woman expecting a child, a woman with an embryo or fetus in her uterus.

PREMATURE BIRTH

Birth of a baby before the normal nine-month period has expired but after about the twenty-eighth week when the fetus can live outside its mother's body.

PRENATAL

Referring to the period prior to birth; the period of pregnancy.

PROCREATION

The process by which a husband and wife reproduce a child through mating; reproduction.

PROMISCUITY

Indiscriminate immoral relations.

PROSTITUTE

A woman who engages in sexual intercourse for money as a livelihood; a harlot.

PUBERTY

Sexual maturity or the earliest age at which a person is able to reproduce; occurs at about twelve years of age for girls and at about fourteen years of age for boys. Puberty is marked by certain physical changes, such as the development of the breasts in girls and the growth of the beard for boys.

PUBIC REGION

That area of the abdomen where the sex organs are found.

REPRODUCTION

The process whereby new individuals are brought to life through the mating of father and mother; procreation.

RH FACTOR

A chemical substance present in the red blood cells of most persons. Serious effects may be suffered by an infant of an Rh-positive father and an Rh-negative mother. This condition is very rare. A blood test during early stages of a pregnancy will determine any such condition which may be serious to the baby. The physician may then take necessary precautions.

SCROTUM

The pouch of skin behind the penis containing the male testes.

SECRETION

The substances produced by the glands. The secretions of the endocrine glands are called hormones.

SEMEN

The fluid produced by the testes. It contains sperm cells.

SEMINAL EMISSION

The discharge of semen from the penis during sleep. It is frequently accompanied by a dream known as a "wet dream."

SEX CELL

The sperm cell of the male and the ovum of the female.

SEX COMPLEX

An abnormal preoccupation with sexual matters and thoughts, wherein non-sexual things arouse sexual associations.

SEXUAL INTERCOURSE

Mating; the uniting of the penis and vagina; coitus, copulation.

SPERM

The male reproductive cell, which starts a new life by joining with an ovum; spermatozoan.

STERILE

A man or woman who is physically unable to reproduce children.

SUBLIMATION

The channeling of sexual energies and tensions into nonsexual and approved outlets, such as sports, dramatics, social and Christian activities.

TESTES

The two male reproductive glands, that manufacture sperm cells and the male sex hormones; testicles. The testes are enclosed in the scrotum.

TRUNK

The part of the body between the neck and the legs; the chest and abdomen together.

UMBILICAL CORD

The rope-like structure connecting the embryo or fetus to the placenta, and carrying nourishment and oxygen from the mother to the baby.

URINE

The waste fluids from the kidneys discharged through the penis of the male and through the vulva of the female.

UTERUS

The chamber where a baby develops before birth, located in the lower part of the woman's abdomen, at the head of the vagina; the womb.

VAGINA

The passage from the uterus to the outside of the woman's body; the birth canal; the place where sperm cells are deposited by the penis during mating.

VENEREAL DISEASE

A disease communicated most often through sexual intercourse with an infected person.

VERNIX

The fatty substance covering the skin of a newly born baby.

VIRGIN

A woman, especially a young woman, who has had no sexual intercourse. May also refer to a young man of the same state.

VULVA

The two pairs of lips forming the outside part of the female sex organ; the entrance to the vagina.

"WET DREAM"

The discharge of semen from the penis during sleep; a normal function usually accompanied by a dream; nocturnal or seminal emission.

WOMB

The uterus; the organ which houses the unborn baby inside its mother.

Part II — Christian Terms

BORN AGAIN

The experience of the new birth; the Holy Spirit comes to dwell in the person who has taken Jesus Christ as Saviour and Lord, implanting spiritual life, eternal life, and giving him a new nature (John 1:12, 13; 3:3-8).

CHRIST

The Saviour who was promised in the Old Testament and revealed in the New Testament in the Person of Jesus of Nazareth, the Son of God, who came to die for people's sins and to redeem them to God (Matthew 16:16; I Peter 3:18).

CHRISTIAN

A person, born again, a child of God; anyone, whether of Jewish or Gentile background, who is trusting Jesus Christ as Saviour and is obeying Him as Lord; one who is indwelt by the Spirit of God (Romans 8:9-11, 14-17).

CONSECRATION

The giving of one's whole self and life, including time, money, talent, thoughts and career, to the Lord Jesus Christ for worship and for service (Romans 12:1).

CONVERSION

Being born again, which is the experience of having one's sins forgiven and one's life completely changed and turned about to follow Christ. This initial step in the Christian life is brought about by repenting of (feeling sorry for and turning from) past sins and beginning to trust Jesus Christ as Saviour and Lord (Matthew 18:3; Acts 3:19).

FAITH

Complete trust and confidence in the Person of the Lord Jesus Christ both for forgiveness of sins and for every daily need in living the Christian life. It is the commitment of one's whole life and eternal destiny to Christ (Hebrews 11:1; Acts 16:31).

HOLY SPIRIT

The Spirit of God; the third Person of the Trinity. He enters the life at the time of the individual's salvation, dwells within, empowers him, and gives him a new nature (John 14-16; Romans 8).

INSPIRATION OF BIBLE

The action of the Holy Spirit in delivering the message of the Bible to its writers and in keeping them free from error while they were recording it (II Timothy 3:16; II Peter 1:21).

JESUS

The Christ, the virgin born Son of God, who came to earth to die for men's sins. He rose again that He might give them new life, and He now has returned to heaven to represent His own. He has promised to return for those who believe in Him (Mark 1:1; Matthew 1:21; I Corinthians 15).

LORD

Jesus Christ is the rightful Master and Sovereign of the whole universe and of every born again person, because He created us all and died to save us (Philippians 2:5-11).

NEW BIRTH

The experience of being born again as a child of God (John 1:12, 13; 3:3-8).

SALVATION

The transaction with God whereby a person who trusts in the crucified and risen Christ as Saviour and Lord is forgiven of sins and is given eternal life (Acts 4:12; Romans 1:16, 17).

SAVED PERSON

One who is forgiven and born again by trusting Jesus Christ as Saviour and Lord. He is thereby freed from sin's ultimate consequences, which are eternal death and separation from God (Titus 3:5-7; Acts 2:21; 4:12; Romans 10:9, 10; I Timothy 2:4).

SCRIPTURE

The sixty-six fully inspired books of the Holy Bible; the Old and New Testaments, which reveal to man God's loving plan to redeem the lost through the death and resurrection of Jesus Christ (II Timothy 3:14-17; Luke 24:25-27).

SIN

Any act, thought, or intention which is contrary to God and His will as revealed in Scripture; that which separates men from God and earns for them His just condemnation; that which is erased and forgiven through faith in Christ (Romans 3:23; 3:10-19).

SIN NATURE

The nature that causes people to sin and to disobey God; every person's nature until the time he is born again and receives a new nature by the Holy Spirit (Romans 5:12; II Corinthians 5:17; Isaiah 64:6).

TESTIMONY

A person's own account of his salvation. The relating of his growth, present status and relationship to Christ (I John 1:1-4).

THE ZONDERVAN PAPERBACK SERIES
Each 95¢

YOU CAN WITNESS WITH CONFIDENCE —
Rosalind Rinker   No. 10714s

FIND FREEDOM — Billy Graham   No. 9716p

THE YEARS THAT COUNT — Rosalind Rinker   No. 10715s

PLAY BALL! — James Hefley   No. 9797s

LIFE IS FOR LIVING — Betty Carlson   No. 9384s

SCIENCE RETURNS TO GOD — James H. Jauncey   No. 9927s

NEVER A DULL MOMENT — Eugenia Price   No. 10584s

SO YOU'RE A TEENAGE GIRL — Jill Renich   No. 10706s

ABOVE OURSELVES — James H. Jauncey   No. 9950s

THE OPEN HEART — Rosalind Rinker   No. 10718p

BUT GOD! — V. Raymond Edman   No. 9555s

FIND OUT FOR YOURSELF — Eugenia Price   No. 10603s

THE SAVING LIFE OF CHRIST — W. Ian Thomas   No. 10908s

YOUR CHILD — Anna B. Mow   No. 12256s

SAY 'YES' TO LIFE — Anna B. Mow   No. 10383s

KNOWING GOD'S SECRETS — John Hunter   No. 9883s

THEY FOUND THE SECRET — V. Raymond Edman   No. 9564s

WE'RE NEVER ALONE — Eileen Guder   No. 9710s

MAN TO MAN — Richard C. Halverson   No. 6818s

A WOMAN'S WORLD — Clyde M. Narramore   No. 12230p

LIFE AND LOVE — Clyde M. Narramore   No. 10412p

YOUNG ONLY ONCE — Clyde M. Narramore   No. 10414s

LIMITING GOD — John Hunter   No. 9884s

GAMES FOR ALL OCCASIONS—Carlson and Anderson   No. 9051p

WOMAN TO WOMAN — Eugenia Price   No. 10589p

PILGRIM'S PROGRESS — John Bunyan   No. 6610s

BILLY GRAHAM — John Pollock   No. 10571p

5500 QUESTIONS AND ANSWERS ON THE WHOLE BIBLE   No. 9624p